Born on the Isle of Man, and now living in the Manx countryside with her blacksmith husband and daughter, Sue King has enjoyed a varied career ranging from broadcasting to hospitality. While living in New Zealand in the 1980s she spent a memorable evening at Circus Oz and it was this experience that inspired her, many years later, to investigate the circus stories connected to her birth place.

'Evenings of Wonder' is a vivid chronicle of the extraordinary circus personalities that visited the Isle of Man in the nineteenth century. All the named characters and events described within these pages are based on fact and background details are as historically accurate as possible. The narrative is a product of the author's imagination. To marry the two has not been an easy balancing act – but then, there is nothing easy about the circus. They just make it look that way.

Evening Dreams of Wonder,
The Theme of General Admiration.
Great Success – and Thunders of Applause.

Advertisement for William Batty's Circus
published in the Manx Liberal, June 24th 1843
(Courtesy of Manx National Heritage)

Best wishes
Sue King

EVENINGS OF WONDER

Sue King

First published in Great Britain in paperback by
Sue King
www.sueking-writer.com
with the support of
Culture Vannin
Fairfield House, Main Road, St Johns,
Isle of Man, IM4 3NA

A CIP catalogue record for this book is available from the British Library

ISBN: 978-1-9161121-0-0

Designed by Sue King
Cover by Ruth Sutherland
Typeset, printed and bound by
Words & Spaces, Taggart House, Douglas,
Isle of Man, IM2 1QD

For Allan, with my love

Evenings of Wonder

Chapter One

THE ROPE YARD

1802 Thursday 22nd July

The island has been all but invisible for much of the day. Since dawn a thick white sea mist has cocooned the coastline, slowing movement in towns and villages and reducing voices to ghostly whispers. It is a regular occurrence in July, often welcomed by islanders as a means of hiding their homeland from unwanted attention.

This evening, however, there are some who are glad the mist has begun to retreat. As it dissolves into pale tendrils and drifts gently out of Douglas harbour, waves of laughter, light-hearted chatter and raucous banter can be heard rising from William Lewin's rope yard on the Quay. A large crowd has gathered in the yard and they're noisy and restless with anticipation. Not that they're expecting to do trade with Mr Lewin. The main business of the day is long over and there's little sense of any commercial propriety.

It would seem this motley assembly has a far more compelling reason to gather in Mr Lewin's yard on a cool summer's evening. According to a recent flurry of handbills and newspaper advertisements they're to be treated to a thrilling variety of equestrian and gymnastic feats known in popular parlance as a circus.

And they certainly have good reason to be garrulous. While mainland Britons have been enjoying the daring delights of the circus for more than three decades, the Isle of Man has been woefully lacking in such diversions, largely due to the unpredictable stretch of water that governs travel between the island and England. This visit by the circus of Mr Ireland and Mr Woolford showcasing their 'Surprising Feats of Activity' is an event to be savoured.

The names of the circus principals are already familiar to newspaper readers. Mr Ireland is renowned for his 'lofty tumbling', leaping high into the air with or without the aid of a springboard, a talent that's earned him the sobriquet of the 'Yorkshire Grasshopper'. His partner Mr Woolford is known as the 'Polish Olympian' for his ability on the pole, the moving ladder, a stack of chairs or a moving horse – in fact anything that requires a sense of equilibrium. To make up a full programme of entertainment the two principals will be joined in the rope yard by a young Irish couple by the name of Short who excel in tumbling, rope walking and juggling.

The island is certainly favoured by the company's visit. A busy summer season has already seen them traverse Ireland and the north of England, and their arrival in Douglas yesterday evening was preceded by an arduous twenty-hour journey from Liverpool on a trading vessel stacked high with bales of cotton and hemp. Thankfully the sea was calm but incessant torrential rain forced the passengers to find shelter and what little comfort they could in every available corner of the ship, crammed tightly into the small, fetid cabin or out on deck squeezed beneath dripping overhangs.

The company's horses – handsome, long-suffering beasts - were tethered beneath a tarpaulin for the entire journey.

As a gun announced the ship's approach to Douglas harbour the island's landscape, or what little was visible through the deluge, had presented an intriguing tableau. The southern side of the river estuary is dominated by a steep, rugged headland of grey rock covered with tough pasture and bracken, guarded at the base by a magnificent castellated mansion house. Below the mansion runs a wide river lined with a narrow shingle bank that accommodates a lime kiln and a row of long, low sheds for the curing of herring.

By contrast the land on the northern side of the estuary is flat and low-lying, crowded with buildings and protected from harsh seas by an impressive, wide sandstone pier. The Red Pier, as it's known, stretches over five hundred feet into the bay and is furnished at the end with an attractive pepper-pot lighthouse. From the base of the pier a genteel avenue of grand houses known as The Parade extends behind the town's northern shoreline to a rocky outcrop topped by a small, circular stone fort. A line of tightly-packed dwellings then follows the edge of a long, curved bay bordered with white sand and backed by heather-clad hills, gradually thinning until all that can be seen is a scattering of small, thatched cottages and grand villas.

With the rain showing little sign of abating, Ireland, Woolford and company were thankful that high tide allowed their vessel to dock quickly alongside the Red Pier, jostling for space between fishing smacks, tall sailing ships and coal boats. In fine weather locals take to the wide pier to promenade or sit on the stone seating and be entertained by singers, musicians and jugglers but on this inclement evening it was deserted save for damp porters. As soon as the horses were off-loaded and the company's trunks were stacked into waiting carts, they made a hasty retreat to their nearby lodgings in the 'old town', a rough triangle of land hidden behind the Parade, crowded with taverns, rundown cottages, ship yards, curing sheds and chandlers - a grim, dark place, intersected by narrow, twisty lanes that have long proved a boon to the island's profitable running trade. Not that the performers were concerned by their surroundings. Weary from their long journey their attention was drawn more to the prospect of a hearty supper and comfortable beds.

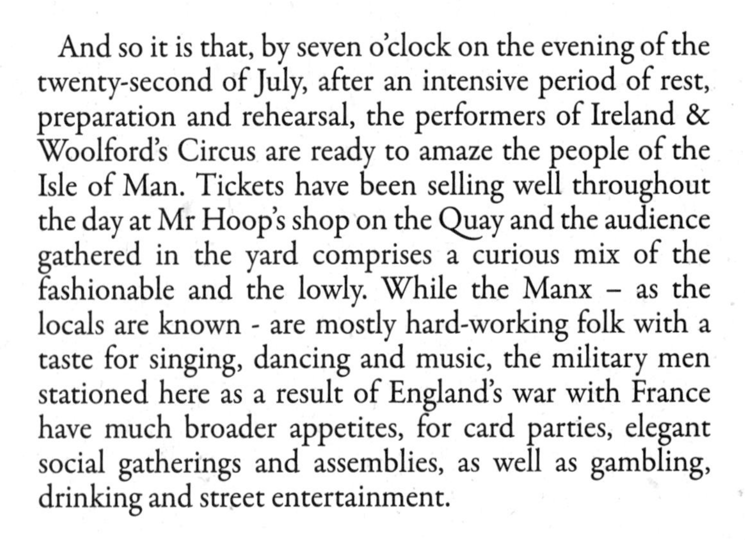

And so it is that, by seven o'clock on the evening of the twenty-second of July, after an intensive period of rest, preparation and rehearsal, the performers of Ireland & Woolford's Circus are ready to amaze the people of the Isle of Man. Tickets have been selling well throughout the day at Mr Hoop's shop on the Quay and the audience gathered in the yard comprises a curious mix of the fashionable and the lowly. While the Manx – as the locals are known - are mostly hard-working folk with a taste for singing, dancing and music, the military men stationed here as a result of England's war with France have much broader appetites, for card parties, elegant social gatherings and assemblies, as well as gambling, drinking and street entertainment.

As the evening sun breaks through the last of the mist and the sky above the yard turns pink, smart soldiers rub shoulder to shoulder with coarse sailors, grimy children squeeze between dapper lawyers and pale-faced shopkeepers, and delicate young ladies dressed in muslin gowns cover their noses to curb the strong odour of the ruddy-cheeked herring girls who hover on the edges of the yard.

It is left to Mr Ireland to quell the hubbub with a swift introduction. After thanking the crowd for their patronage he declares that the opening act of Ireland and Woolford's marvellous circus will be a performance on the slack wire and tight ropes by 'the inimitable Mrs Short' and with a flourish he steps aside to allow for the entrance of a small, dainty woman dressed in a simple white chemise gown, satin slippers and a turban adorned with green feathers. Her appearance is greeted with rousing applause, as much for the delicacy of her slight figure as for the daunting equipment she is about to perform on. On the periphery of the exhibition area one of Mr Lewin's finest thick hemp ropes has been staked into the ground and guided up through two heavy timber poles fixed as an A-frame, ten feet high, then allowed to dangle loosely above the floor for twenty feet or so before being tied to another A-frame and stretched down to a metal stake at the other end.

Mr Ireland steps forward to help Mrs Short stand on the middle of the rope at its lowest point and for a few heart-stopping seconds her entire body wobbles as she finds her balance. Then, with slim arms outstretched and waving in an undulating motion, Mrs Short places one foot almost sideways in front of the other and slowly makes her way up the rope, which sways the entire time. Her eyes appear to be fixed on a point in the distance but as she turns and walks in the other direction, she pauses every now and then to cast a sweet, sidelong smile at her enraptured audience.

After a minute or two Mr Ireland re-appears and begins to pass her a variety of objects – china plates, pipes, cards, even a sword – which she balances on her head or passes from one hand to the other and behind her back. With the young children in the audience exclaiming loudly, she is then passed a small round table, two glasses and a decanter – all of which she places carefully on the rope, before helping herself to wine without spilling a drop, the rope swinging all the while.

To vigorous clapping and a ripple of excited chatter, Mrs Short dismounts the rope and prepares for her next act – the tight rope. As she rests on a chair to the side of the circle, wiping her hands and rubbing chalk on the soles of her slippers, other members of the company adjust the tension on the rope until it is tight and horizontal. A ladder helps her to the mounting position, once again the crowd holds its breath and Mrs Short walks as easily across the rope as if she were walking on solid ground, a long thin pole to aid her balance her only prop.

But that is not the limit of her talents. As a flute player hidden on the sidelines strikes up a familiar hornpipe melody Mrs Short dispenses with the pole and proceeds to dance on the rope. With arms akimbo and legs and feet flying out to each side in sharp, rhythmic movements this bold and fearless young woman gives the impression of being as grounded as a sailor on the deck of a sailing ship.

While some spectators are shocked by Mrs Short's wild exertions, the general assembly are greatly appreciative of her abilities – and the quality of Mr Lewin's rope - and it is to loud 'hurrahs' and cheers that she delicately climbs down from the tightrope, gives a quick curtsy and flits into the shadows. As she does so a pale shape tumbles past her, a man, as young as herself, dressed in a white linen shirt, pantaloons and leather slippers. Introduced to the audience as Mr Short, the young fellow pauses only long enough to grant the mesmerised men, women and children before him a long, sweeping bow and devilish smile, before proceeding to travel the length of the rope yard in an extraordinary fashion.

From one end to the other he runs, jumps, spins in the air, rolls on the ground, leaps on to his hands once, twice, three times, and finally runs straight up a wooden timber, somersaulting backwards to land on the ground just feet from his audience. The delight of the children is evident, the reaction of the adults a mixture of admiration and alarm at such physical abandonment.

But Mr Short is merely the curtain raiser. With barely a moment for the audience to gather breath, it is the turn of the talented Mr Woolford to take to the tight rope. This lean and agile gentleman climbs nimbly to the top of the tight rope platform and, completely unaided, fairly runs to the centre of the rope where he proceeds to bounce, slowly at first but gathering in pace until his body is lifting into the air, his shirt gently inflating and deflating with every movement. As the watching crowd jostle for a better view he leaps high into the air, a good ten feet or so, landing perfectly each time on the elastic rope, his knees bending and arms extending to maintain his balance. At one point, while in mid-air, he even appears to defy gravity by completely stopping, frozen in time, for two or three seconds.

A shouted command to a company man and a skipping rope is thrown up to him. For a dozen or so twirls he skips deftly on the spot in the centre of the tightrope. The skipping rope is then discarded and replaced with a hoop which he holds with both hands and swings widely over his head, hopping on the spot in small, perfectly judged movements. This too, is then discarded and a small wooden chair is thrown up to him which he tosses lightly from side to side. The chair has a bottom strut which allows him to place it on the rope and sit upon it, balanced and steady, before miming the eating of a large meal. Only the pretence of a hearty belch, accompanied by a wicked grin, breaks the spell of hushed attention and brings about guffaws of laughter.

The tightrope, however, is not Mr Woolford's only skill. Having returned to 'terra firma' he briefly leaves the staging area, re-emerging with a tall wooden ladder with wide rungs. Holding the ladder upright with his hands on the sides, he places his feet at the edges of the bottom rung and steadily rocks it from side to side, lifting the feet of the ladder and thus making it appear to 'walk'. As he does so he gradually climbs higher up the rungs until he is able to fling one leg over the top, brace both feet either side of the top rung and continue to move the ladder in a full circle by leaning slightly from left to right, using his weight to lift the ladder and move it in tiny steps. By maintaining his balance both hands are now free to juggle with a set of wooden clubs thrown to him from the dim recesses of the yard, an act of such astonishing confidence that the people of Douglas can hardly believe their eyes. His performance concluded, Mr Woolford dismounts from the ladder and with a flourish and a bow acknowledges the generous applause of the audience and disappears behind the stacked coils of rope that make up the wings of the improvised stage.

Hardly have the audience time to discuss his exploits, however, before their attention is called to an announcement by Mr Short introducing the Original Flying Phenomenon, Mr Ireland, whose physical agility without the aid of any spring board is guaranteed to astound and amaze! He looks to his left and all eyes follow him as a large bay horse is led into the middle of the rope yard, snorting and nodding its head. The man holding the horse's head collar pushes its hindquarters around until it is standing side on to the crowd. Then, suddenly, from the darkness, a figure bounds into the clearing, and before the audience can work out what's happening, the figure leaps into the air, braces his hands on the horse's rump, and flies, legs outstretched, over the animal's head, lands with a 'whoomph' in the sawdust on the other side, rolls head first and quickly rises to his feet, body erect, arms to the sky. As he does so the stable-hand flings himself up onto the horse's back and flattens himself across its withers. Mr Ireland, 'the Yorkshire Grasshopper', then takes another long run up towards the horse and justifies his nickname by leaping with extraordinary energy over both man and beast, clearing the stable-hand's head by a whisker. The crowd are suitably impressed. Even more so as word has it that this young athlete's career nearly ended recently after injuries sustained at the Royal Circus in London. His physical prowess is breath-taking.

The horse having been led away, the scene is set for an even greater variety of physically challenging tasks. Mr Woolford and Mr Short enter the arena, one carrying a pole above his head, the other a large hoop made of twisted fibres on the end of a stick. At the covered end of the arena a canvas bag has also been suspended from the ceiling, high above the ground. To growing encouragement from the crowd, no longer overawed into silence, Mr Ireland takes himself to the furthest point of the yard and stands still for a minute or so, breathing deeply with eyes closed. With sweat running down his brow, his hair flattened damply to his head, he rocks back and forward on his heels, clenching and unclenching his fists. As the men in the crowd stamp their feet and the ladies flutter their fans, a man carrying a flaming torch moves forward and lights the hoop carried by Mr Short. At that bright signal, Mr Ireland launches into a run and with three giant hops leaps through the flaming hoop, rolls on the ground, leaps high over Mr Woolford's pole and finally flings himself sideways into the air, at the same time kicking the canvas bag with his right foot. There's no holding the audience back now. Their appreciation can be heard all the way down the Quay.

But there's little opportunity for the performers to wallow in approbation. A shout goes up to 'bring on the horses'. Five local animals have been hired to accompany their own two and all seven are brought into the yard and lined up in a tight row, adjacent to a large wooden springboard. The horses are so close to one another their flanks are almost touching and they're edgy and nervous, tossing their heads and flattening their ears. Three young men hold their head collar ropes in a fierce grip to steady them as Mr Ireland once again takes himself to the end of the yard. While he focusses on his next manoeuvre Mr Woolford urges the audience into as near a silence as they can muster. The animals are impatient, clattering their feet, shuffling and snorting, until Mr Ireland raises himself up on the balls of his feet and shoots forward as though fired from a cannon. As his feet hit the springboard he is hurled into the air and skims cleanly over the backs of all seven horses who pull against their ropes in panic, shaking their heads and rolling their eyes.

With a tight curl of his body Mr Ireland lands inelegantly in a large pile of straw on the other side, sparking a new round of applause and loud cheers as the horses are led away. All props are then pushed to one side and the three male performers draw the evening to a close by rapidly flipping backwards and forwards across the yard, culminating with an energetic flourish of high somersaults.

When it becomes clear that the performance has finished, the crowd stamp their feet, bawling loudly, loathe to accept that the extraordinary display they've just witnessed is really over. It's only after the tumblers have been joined by Mrs Short for a prolonged and enthusiastic ovation, and an announcement by Mr Ireland of a further week of evening performances, that the men, women and children of Douglas begin to drift away, their chatter a mixture of admiration, wonder and tut-tutting. Sedan chairs carry away the town's most distinguished ladies, while those gentlemen who have no need to rise early in the morning make for the nearest inn to discuss their verdicts over pipes and port.

For the company, however, there is no respite. The hour is late, order has yet to be restored in the rope yard, and victuals and sleep are more important to the tumblers than jugs of ale. Tomorrow they will rise early, rehearse all day and in the evening repeat their demanding tricks to yet another mesmerised audience. In a week's time they will pack away their costumes and props, board the packet boat in Douglas harbour and head for the Lancashire coast and a very different engagement at the Preston Guild.

For now though, Messrs Ireland, Woolford and company can commend themselves on successfully introducing the Isle of Man to the thrills of the circus. The extraordinary spectacle in Mr Lewin's rope yard will be talked about for years to come. A new era of entertainment has begun.

Addendum

The following year Ireland & Woolford performed in Hull, adding a new pantomime called the Harlequin Mariner directed by Mrs Ireland.

By summer 1810 the company had been joined by Master Woolford 'the infant equestrian' performing a flag dance and hornpipe.

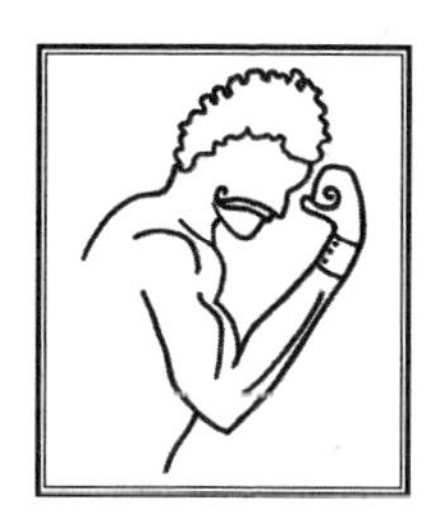

Chapter Two

THE STRONG MAN

1811 Saturday 28th December

He is a tall man, an exceptionally tall man, six foot six inches in his stockinged feet, and strikingly handsome, with the large straight nose, shapely eyebrows and lustrous black hair so distinctive of his Paduan forefathers. His broad shoulders, thick neck and wide chest create an immediate impression of bovine strength, yet his movements are lithe and almost graceful, his legs and lower torso long and lean.

Prior to his performance, he lowers his head to converse with the manager of the Assembly Room and the flimsy, satin-robed creatures in the audience, of whom there is quite a number, lean in to try and catch his words. A fierce winter storm is raging outside in Douglas Bay and his voice has to compete with the sound of the sea crashing against the bulnoses at the rear of the building.

On such a turbulent night the ladies in the audience are strangely reassured by the sheer presence of this living giant and his Mediterranean accent gives rise to a heightened level of rustling and twittering. They become increasingly impatient for his performance to begin. Fortunately, however, they don't have long to wait and the evening commences.

The spectators fall quiet. The tension is palpable. Giovanni Battista Belzoni, 'Strongman and Showman Extraordinaire', fresh from appearances in London, Dublin and Portugal, commands the attention of his breathless audience – and catches them quite off guard with an opening act of startling delicacy and finesse.

Standing perfectly still in the centre of the small stage, Belzoni slowly bends to a collection of variously-filled drinking glasses arranged on a table in front of him and by merely running his long, brown fingers along their rims elicits the most exquisite music. The sound is sweet, unexpected and delicious. Even the background shrieks and howls of the storm outside can't compete with the manmade overtures created by this Italian marvel.

The packed room is warm and stuffy and the women seated disconcertingly close to Signor Belzoni can barely breathe. But this is only the beginning. Shortly he's handed an instrument unfamiliar to his audience, a stringed lute that he introduces as an 'an-JELL-ika'. Moving to a tall stool, he carefully balances the instrument on his powerful thighs and skilfully plucks at it with a concentrated fervour that draws enthusiastic applause from the room.

As the evening progresses Signor Belzoni increasingly amazes the spellbound assembly with a variety of unusual entertainments that become more and more daring as the clock ticks by. Yet it's not until just after ten o'clock that his repertoire becomes truly shaped by his physical talents. Stripped to the waist and wearing only cream stockinet pants modestly embellished with a large green silk leaf, he takes to the centre of the stage, illuminated by a dozen candelabra, to recreate the sculptured forms of Ancient Greece in a variety of classical poses.

Such use of the human form to entertain has never before been seen in this town and the genteel citizens of Douglas are unsure how to react. Belzoni's bronzed, naked skin, perfect stillness and muscular control are at once both shocking and riveting and the crowd's reaction is conveyed as a ripple of nervous rumblings, urgent whispers and slow hand-claps, weighted by the airlessness of the room and the close contact of its occupants.

It is the final sections of Belzoni's performance, however, which leave his ardent new followers in no doubt as to his claim to the title of 'Strongman and Showman Extraordinaire'.

After a hasty costume change he now appears as 'The Patagonian Samson', dressed in a short, leopard-skin tunic and pale silk tights that highlight his sharply defined calf muscles. Studded leather cuffs encircle his wrists and his feet are banded by leather Roman sandals. As he waits centre stage a large, heavy coach wheel is carried on to the platform and placed in front of him. With a deep intake of breath he braces his back, grips the wheel with both hands and, assisted by two stage hands, raises it skyward. Tilting his head backwards and pushing his chest forwards, the wheel is carefully balanced on his jutting chin and the assistants step away. The audience gasp, pause for a breathless second or two, then break into fervent applause and enthusiastic hollering.

On the stage Signor Belzoni is sweating profusely. His heavily muscled arms glisten, his black, wavy hair and thick, handlebar moustache gleam in the flickering light and the tendons in his neck stand out like whipcords, taut and shining. For a fraction longer than is necessary the wheel remains on his chin, quivering slightly, until the two assistants step forward to take the weight. On the release of the wheel Signor Belzoni takes a long, slow bow, gathering his composure before his next display of skill and balance.

Presently, a young boy is introduced to the audience. He's eight years old or so, slightly built, barefoot and dressed in an Arabic-style tunic, with a colourful belt and turban-like headdress. As he waits, attentive and wide-eyed, Signor Belzoni produces a long, sturdy wooden pole. The child watches the towering Italian closely as he takes up the pole and, with help from his assistants, proceeds to balance it on the top of his head. One of the assistants then links his hands in a cradle, allowing the boy to leap lightly up onto Belzoni's shoulder and thence shimmy up to the top of the pole, gripping it like a monkey with his hands and bare feet, his head bent against the ceiling rafters. The boy is heard to mutter 'Si' and Signor Belzoni steps forward a pace. The pole sways but the boy hangs on, causing the men in the audience to roar with approval and stamp their feet. Close to the front of the stage a woman, pale and clammy, faints into her companion's arms. As the boy descends from the pole and disappears behind a curtain Belzoni allows himself a small smile before he too ducks out of sight.

A short interval follows in which the audience chatter like a flock of starlings, falling quiet only when the strong man returns to stand facing the room, arms crossed, while his two assistants strap a heavy metal belt to his waist, solid metal girders extruding on either side. The weight of the belt alone is more than most ordinary men can bear, but then seven young men appear, dressed in similar fashion to the young boy, in baggy pantaloons, white muslin shirts and flamboyant head dresses. As Signor Belzoni steadies his feet against the bare wooden boards of the stage the young men spring up onto the metal frame, one by one, until all seven are forming a rough pyramid around his body. At this point Belzoni, his strained muscles trembling, closes his eyes and slowly raises his arms to the ceiling. The young men take this as a signal and outstretch their own arms as the audience break into one last long and enthusiastic uproar.

He has triumphed; the Isle of Man has been won. Giovanni Battista Belzoni is beyond doubt 'The King of the Strong Men'.

As the crowds leave the Assembly Room and head out into the wild, black night and their waiting carriages, Belzoni retreats to the back room where the manager, Mr Downward, has prepared him a plate of bread, cheese and salt pork and a glass of Madeira. The Italian is exhausted and grateful. He's only been on the Island a few days, following a hellish, storm-tossed journey from Dublin on the packet boat, and prior to that was performing at numerous fairs and circuses in Ireland and Europe. With the fierce gales delaying his onward travel to England for another week the hastily arranged performances at the Assembly Room have been most welcome, covering the costs of an extended stay for Belzoni, his wife Sarah and their company of young assistants.

And this is both the first and last time that the people of the Isle of Man will be able to witness his extraordinary talents. Belzoni has already confided in Mr Downward that, on completing this tour of three Kingdoms, he wishes to retire from the world of showmanship and pursue a career that challenges his intellect as well as his body. A fascination with hydraulic engineering and the wonders of Egypt is drawing him to the Land of the Pharoahs where he hopes to discover the secrets of ancient civilisation. Years of honing his strength and developing a sound physique will, he believes, be a distinct advantage in the tough conditions of the desert where he's heard tombs and treasures are waiting to be explored. Mr Downward listens intently as Belzoni steers the conversation seamlessly from engineering to art, history to antiquities, revealing a surprising breadth of knowledge and understanding of each subject. That Belzoni will succeed if he reaches the sand dunes of North Africa seems hardly in doubt.

As a cold, biting wind screeches through gaps in the roof of the Assembly Room and the pounding of the sea reaches a crescendo, Mr Downward feels a strange envy for this erudite titan with his unusual talents and desire for adventure. Such fearlessness. Such extraordinary passions. The name Giovanni Battista Belzoni will surely be a name to remember.

Addendum

In September 1818 Manx newspapers reported that the statue of Memnon found at Thebes had been deposited in the British Museum. The ten-ton head was moved under the direction of Belzoni.

The following year it was claimed that the importance of Belzoni's discoveries in Egypt were of great interest to all lovers of science.

In November 1821 Belzoni 'the celebrated traveller' was a guest at a grand dinner given by the new Lord Mayor of London.

In October 1823 Belzoni, now habitually dressed in Moorish clothing, attempted to explore the African interior via the river Benin. In December he fell gravely ill with dysentery and wrote to a friend saying that he did not expect to survive, that he would die as a beggar and if any of his friends could help his family that any monies should be divided between his faithful wife Sarah and his mother.

In May 1824 Manx newspapers announced the death of the great strongman and adventurer Giovanni Battista Belzoni.

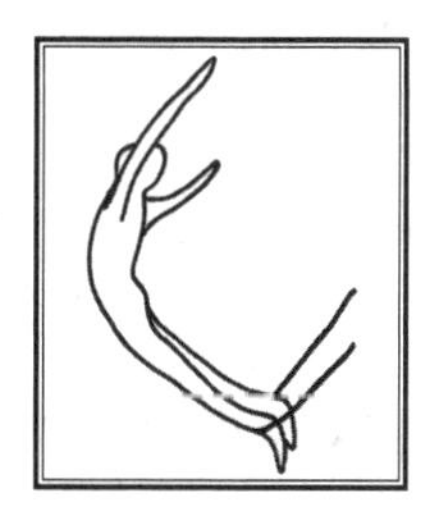

Chapter Three

THE COACH YARD

1826 Saturday 9th September

It's September, a cool, grey morning, and for hours now, since just after daybreak, the sound of incessant activity has been emanating from Mr Dixon's livery stables on the Parade near the Red Pier. Nails being hammered, the heavy thud of wood on wood, bellowed instructions – often in dialects unfamiliar to the Manx ear - and the clatter of horse's hooves on stone cobbles. Townsfolk going about their business nearby are naturally curious but the gate to the stables is shut and a young lad, paid threepence for his trouble, stands guard to fend off unwanted visitors. Only a colourful bill pasted on an adjacent wall hints at the reason for the temporary closure of the stables. It announces the advent of a fortnight of extraordinary entertainment, the like of which hasn't been seen on the island for nearly a quarter of a century. And it could not be more welcome.

Since the earliest days of summer the talk has been all about the weather. At the outset, a long hot dry spell brought mixed fortunes for locals trying to earn a living. Lodging houses welcomed the large influx of visitors who arrived from England to enjoy the island's fine bathing and restorative sea air, but the lack of rain was no good for farmers who watched their new crops shrivel and die under the white sun and endless blue skies. Then, in late August, the high temperatures exploded in a deluge of heavy rain and fierce winds. With the Irish Sea a treacherous cauldron the Manx fishing fleet was confined to harbour, deliveries of food and mail from the mainland were severely curtailed and Douglas fell prey to morbid outbreaks of dysentery. Against such a grim backdrop the atmosphere in the town quickly became unsettled. While residents, well adapted to insular isolation, were happy to amuse themselves with card games, dancing and the occasional ball, the strangers in town wanted more.

There have been a few varieties to keep them entertained. During the early fine spell the boards of the town's elegant little theatre were graced by some of Britain's finest actors and, every now and then, a daring entertainment has surfaced to confound even the most disbelieving – jugglers, ventriloquists, conjurors and flamboyant pyrotechnicists. But just lately such amusements have been thin on the ground and now that the gales have abated, locals and visitors alike are keen to welcome something a little meatier. Especially if it offers a distraction from talk of the weather.

It is then immaculate timing that Douglas should now greet the arrival of Kinlochs' Circus - a highly experienced troop of equestrians and performers led by a former artistic director and manager of Cooke's renowned Olympic Circus in Liverpool.

And Mr Kinloch is also pleased to be here. Douglas has the air of a progressive town, the dirty, cramped, old quarter fast being outgrown by smart new streets that accommodate the island's wealthy merchants and growing swell of business entrepreneurs. On the hill overlooking the town, open farmland has been replaced by a long, elegant terrace named Athol Street in honour of the Island's former Duke. Its tall houses face east over the harbour and the air that drifts in through their sash windows is pure and clear.

Mr Kinloch is also well satisfied with his choice of venue for their engagement. The close proximity of the livery stables to the quayside enabled the circus company to quickly offload and transfer their substantial luggage, livestock and equipment; the stables has a spacious open yard overlooking the small beach that runs between the Red Pier and the old fort, and although the Parade backs onto the old town ingrained with the stink of tanneries and herring houses, many of the dwellings are undeniably grand and populated by gentry with the time and money for entertainment. By a stroke of good fortune the area even boasts a hot-and-cold water bath house which will be most welcomed by weary performers.

In fact, Kinloch's company have been more than a little surprised by the port of Douglas. Expectations of a dull, quiet backwater were quickly quashed by a crowded harbour and quayside humming with life. The narrow, cobbled quay is lined with sail and rope makers' yards and warehouses selling paper, dried fruits, spirits and tobacco. Throughout the day fishermen unload slippery crates of herring and mackerel; coal boats discharge their black cargo into waiting wagons and noisy herds of cattle are driven onto large transport ships in readiness for their passage to England.

As for the people – whether peasant or gentry, merchant or shopkeeper – they all appear eager to catch the latest news and keep up with these fast-changing times. Which bodes well for a circus programme with an international flavour.

As the morning progresses it becomes increasingly evident that the entertainment being offered by Kinloch's Circus will be most unusual. Just after ten o'clock the gate to the livery yard is opened and a small group emerges. One of the men in the group is enormous, a human giant, broad-shouldered with arms like table legs, a tree trunk for a neck and a bald, shiny brown head. By contrast one of his companions is small and lithe, with very dark skin, a boyish figure and shoulder-length black hair tied with a ribbon. They don't converse but it appears to any passer-by that these characters must be from foreign shores. The group disappear round a corner and a few minutes later return with a handcart laden with long coils of thick cotton web rope and large heavy metal fixings, while four strong young men come behind them carrying two, twenty-five feet long timber poles on their shoulders. The group vanish into the yard once more and the noise of hammering resumes. Only when the gates open to the general public just before midday are the mysteries surrounding this new circus company explained – and the eyes of the Manx public opened to a world they can barely conceive.

Twelve o'clock and Mr Dixon's yard is bursting at the seams. Benches and chairs have been provided for the gentry at one and sixpence each, whilst every available standing space has been sold at a shilling a piece – half price for children – to an excited gathering who jostle vigorously for the best view.

As the crowd holler and cheer, Mr Kinloch announces his company's "Grand Performance of The Equestrians!" beginning with a display of still vaulting, an act of extreme agility that familiarises a rider with the rhythm and movement of his horse. Recent reports of the war in France have highlighted the value of skilled horsemanship and now it seems the Manx public are to witness for themselves the extraordinary bond that can be nurtured between man and beast when time and training allow.

Four fit young men enter the yard riding four equally fit and fine horses. Each rider is seated on a thick pad, having dispensed with conventional saddles and stirrups. Mr Kinloch conducts the action with a long whip, bringing the horses up to a steady, measured canter and after only a couple of circuits of the dirt floor the riders begin dismounting and mounting at speed while the horses are still in motion. As the horses' hooves thunder alarmingly close to the front row of the audience the riders fling themselves with apparent ease and lightness of body over the backs of their mounts from alternating sides, to sit facing forward or backwards. After a few minutes two of the horses are quickly turned around to canter clockwise and the audience roar their approval as the opposing circles of movement and vaulting create a dizzying spectacle. The adults clearly find the spectacle thrilling but the noise and whirlwind activity causes babes-in-arms to burst into tears and cling to their parents.

Thankfully, the next act brings a swift change of pace and atmosphere. Strongman Signor Spelterini, 'The Flemish Hercules', specialises in virtuoso displays of brute strength and extraordinary balancing feats. This enormous man (the very same seen leaving the yard earlier to gather materials) may have the appearance of a mythical ogre but he soon has the audience eating out of his hand as he balances a range of items on his jutting chin, beginning with a beautiful, delicate peacock feather. As he works his way up to taking the full weight of a half-ton, solid timber beam on his powerful jaw it seems the thick folds in his bronzed, sweating neck are all that are preventing his head from snapping free of his body.

With an interval announced to allow the setting up of the next act, a clown and two stilt walkers enter the arena to amuse and distract the audience but they have a task to do so. At the rear of the yard half a dozen company men are busying themselves checking the fastness of two tall wooden poles placed upright ten feet apart, manacled to the ground with heavy chains and ropes and braced by a long crossbar. Two large metal bolts are attached to each end of the crossbar and to these are tied a long thick rope that hangs in a vee shape so its lowest point is ten feet or so above the ground.

The clown and stilt walkers do their best to entertain the gawping crowd until a slim young person skips out to stand beneath the high rope and the murmur evolves into a loud clamour. Introduced by Mr Kinloch as 'the Flying Brazilian Pablo Paddington' who will 'dazzle the people of the Isle of Man with his exertions on the Corde Volante!' the young man flings another rope over the lowest point of the main rope and uses his hands and naked feet to shimmy up like a sailor in rigging until he is perched comfortably in the centre of the cord. He then discards his aid rope and grips the cord on either side of him, looking remarkably relaxed and at home. He grins at the crowd, who cheer in response. Many of them are countryfolk who came into town for this morning's weekly market and the idea that you can earn a living from putting your muscles to uses other than manual labour is a revelation.

Pablo Paddington is dressed in a striped cotton shirt, coloured neckerchief and white cotton trousers and his black hair is bundled into a white turban. His skin is nut brown and smooth, his frame taut and well-muscled. Exotic, dark-skinned people are rarely seen on the Island and with Brazil so prominent in the news of late the gentry in the audience are particularly curious to observe his performance. As circus has no need for the spoken word physical ability will be the only language required here.

The audience crane their necks to follow Mr Paddington's every move as he pulls himself up into a standing position. His facial features may be fine and delicate but the strength of his physique is unquestionable.

Pushing his legs forward he urges the rope to start swinging. As he does so he lifts one leg and wraps it around the cord and brings himself back to a sitting position, side on to the audience, his other leg hanging loosely. With casual elegance he leans back on the rope and pretends to smoke a cigar, a move that prompts the audience to huge laughter. For a few minutes, he maintains his relaxed repose, all the while idly swinging high above the yard. Until suddenly, to a shocked gasp from below, Mr Paddington plunges forward, catching the rope behind his knees and dangles perilously, his arms swinging his body to and fro. A few more vigorous swings and he flings his body upward again, grabbing the cord and pulling himself up to a sitting position. With the eyes of the crowd fixed upon his every move he urges the rope to a full swing, high enough that he must surely be able to see over the roof of the stables. Only those with delicate dispositions avert their gaze for fear that the risk and danger is all too real, the rope too high, the ground below all too unforgiving. Once the momentum is at full speed he launches into a series of astonishing 'tourbillons', tumbling forward and revolving like a windmill, the rope apparently passing through his arms. The crowd go wild, cheering, whistling and calling his name, and the yard reverberates with a sense of raw energy. His somersaults completed, Mr Paddington slows the rope to a gentle swing and stands up once again, caressing the cord and elegantly twisting his body around it in imitation of classical poses.

For a moment his graceful, easy movement urges the crowd to a hushed silence. But he's not done with them yet. In a final display of fearless athleticism he slides his body over the rope and tilts into a horizontal position, lying face up with only the rope supporting his lower back. As he once again begins to swing the audience respond with stamping feet and clapping hands. The rope surges forward, backward, forward once more until he suddenly lets go, twirling his whole body in the air in a fast rotating twist. When he lands perfectly back on the centre of the rope the noise from the crowd is deafening, and from the tack room where he waits Mr Kinloch watches on with a feeling of enormous relief.

High above the yard Mr Paddington slows the rope to a halt then slips through it until he hangs by his arms and drops to the ground with all the weight of a feather. The crowd rush forward to get a closer look at him but he dodges their clutches and squirms his way through the melee to the tack room.

Prior to the next act the clown once again blusters his way into the yard, fooling with a large woman who is feeling the heat of the moment, and pretending to steal a farmer's hat. Mr Kinloch dispenses him with wild kicks aimed at his rear end and announces that the afternoon's entertainment is to conclude with a performance of the popular equestrian comedy 'Billy Button or The Tailor's Journey to Brentford'.

Even as Mr Kinloch is speaking a horse enters the yard, ridden by a dishevelled character sloppily dressed in oversized clothing, clutching a book and the measuring sticks of a tailor. The horse appears to have its own agenda and meanders around the yard, nudging Mr Kinloch to a hasty exit as the rider attempts to gain control, fumbling with the reins and saddle. Although the rider is padded out with layers of shirts, waistcoats and overcoats his dark face tells the audience they're once again witnessing a performance by Pablo Paddington and there's renewed laughter as he falls clumsily to the ground and is almost knocked over by his errant mount.

Once mounted up, after a third awkward attempt, Mr Paddington urges the horse to a trot and bounces around the yard, his hat slipping over his eyes. But without clear direction the horse rushes the audience who clutch each other in alarm, a situation exacerbated by the appearance of a squawking flock of geese. As the horse shies, Mr Paddington drops his book and measures and in a vivid gesture of mock fury mimes cutting off the horse's ears with a pair of scissors. At which point the horse has had enough. It rears, throwing its incompetent rider to the ground with a thump.

With the geese flapping and honking and the audience hooting with laughter the remainder of the act dissolves into organised chaos. Even though he manages to hurl himself back into the saddle the inept tailor no longer has the strength to hang on and tumbles dramatically backwards over the horse's rump onto the dirt. Dusty and bothered, he's unprepared when the horse comes up behind him and chases him into the stable block, leaving behind a flock of hysterical geese and an enthusiastic audience who continue to applaud loudly long after the performance has ended.

For a few minutes Pablo Paddington sits in the darkness of the stables while he gets his breath back. A groom takes charge of the horse and leads it away and Pablo begins to peel off the layers of clothing that helped to cushion his falls. His body feels battered and weary and once he's sure the last of the crowd have left through the main gates, leaving only the circus company inside to tidy up, he returns to the tack room and picks up a piece of wet flannel to wipe his face. The cloth quickly turns brown as pale streaks appear on his skin. He dips the flannel in a bucket of water and before long the water is dark brown and his face is no longer the colour of hazelnuts but more like that of fresh cream. He removes his trousers, revealing white legs that end in brown ankles. Finally, he removes his undershirt and carefully releases the stiff bandaging that wraps around his upper torso.

In the place of the 'Flying Brazilian' there now stands a young woman, pale skinned, slim and well-muscled. She is hot and she is tired. But she cannot let her guard down for too long. Another performance later this afternoon means 'Pablo Paddington' is allowed only a brief respite from the making-up box. Mr Kinloch pays good wages and by four o'clock he will expect to get his money's worth.

As Mr Paddington once again flies through the air above the people of Douglas they will witness something they will experience only once in their lifetime. Even if what they think they see is not what they see at all.

Addendum

In 1827 British newspapers reported with great excitement that Pablo Paddington, a circus equestrian posing as a 'man of colour', had been discovered to be a woman.

The discovery did not adversely affect her career and in 1830 'Pablo Paddington' performed in Leeds, billed as the Siamese Aeronaut on the Corde Crescent. Ten years later she was still performing, appearing in Gloucester as 'the Man of Colour' and finishing her set on the corde volante with a dramatic firework display.

Her strongman colleague Signor Spelterini was not so fortunate. In 1831 while balancing a heavy weight on his teeth he dislocated his neck, resulting in almost instant death.

Chapter Four

THE CIRCUS OF DREAMS

1843 Thursday 29th June

As the company bearing his name settles into its 1843 season in Douglas in the Isle of Man, circus proprietor William Batty is entrenched in his warm and stuffy office in the heart of London. Although he'd have dearly loved to visit the island he's heard so much about, his every waking moment is currently pre-occupied with two rather more ambitious circus projects in the capital.

In Lambeth, near Westminster Bridge, William has recently overseen the development of the old swimming baths into a grandiose venue known as the 'Olympic Arena' which now combines athletic, equestrian and comic performances with the comfort and facilities of a first-rate theatre. It's also ensured him of the continued loyalty of London audiences while he rebuilt Astley's famous Amphitheatre, devastated by fire two years ago. By Easter weekend he had this glorious edifice, the true home of the English circus, ready to re-open - bigger, brighter and grander than ever.

But London does not have a monopoly on the desire for good entertainment. For some time, William's been aware that the Isle of Man, a small island in the Irish Sea, is a potential goldmine. The island's residents are known to be increasingly cosmopolitan and open to new experiences, and every summer an organised steamer shipping service now takes many hundreds of visitors to the island for recreation and a change of air. And these visitors are not just gentry who can afford good hotels, roast beef and the finest Madeira but northern manufactory workers who like to spend their precious week's holiday taking day trips around the island, sight-seeing and sea bathing. At night though, what can they do but drink in taverns or visit dark, confined theatres? William Batty knows that, given the chance, these pleasure seekers will be drawn to a circus like moths to a flame.

The lure of a good circus, however, is so much more than bare-chested acrobats and toffee apples at the door. William is content to leave such cheap draws to the penny sideshows and country fairs. His entertainments are about splendour, opulence, thrills and glamour. Visitors to Astley's leave the auditorium feeling breathless and stunned by what they have seen and heard. Their ears ring, their eyes shine, their hands smart from clapping and their jaws ache from enthusiastic clamouring. And it's this sense of wonder that is William Batty's dream for the Isle of Man. The Manx may have seen circus troupes before, but nothing like a Batty's Circus.

Consequently, his starting point was not the lease of a merchant's yard crammed between tight streets but something much bolder. William has promised the Manx public a full two-month season of nightly entertainment, and to this end he appointed London architect Michael

Moss – a man with over thirty years' experience - to organise and manage the construction of a large, self-contained circus building on the outskirts of Douglas.

The location for the building was chosen with great care. A number of factors came into play and the decision to site it on the spacious grazing pasture known as Gick's Field satisfied them all. As soon as Michael Moss walked around the edges of the field on the western slopes above the town he was instantly captivated by its truly splendid situation. Perched on the flattened brow of the hill just above St George's Church, and slightly beyond the last of the town streets, the lush pasture enjoys panoramic views that sweep in a south-north curve from the river to the harbour and thence up to Douglas Head, before taking in the whole blue expanse of Douglas Bay. Chimneys and dark rooftops spread out directly below Gick's Field but the site itself is set in a verdant band of green grass and thick gorse hedgerows, with extensive strawberry and gooseberry market gardens to the southern side and the green avenues and vegetable plots of a country estate to the north.

Michael Moss was also keenly aware of another, more commercially sound reason for setting William Batty's circus in this new location. Gick's Field is not only a stone's throw from affluent and highly desirable Athol Street, with its merchants' residences, schools and chapels, but it also lies adjacent to the main road leading out of town to the west, along which can be found a number of large, new mansions owned by the gentry and the nobility. Here, the circus not only has the open space to create a striking visual impression on the people of Douglas, but is on the very doorsteps of those who have the money to pay for the best seats.

By early May Mr Moss was ready to begin work, gathering around him a strong local workforce of builders, timber suppliers, roofers, painters, decorators and drapers. The extraordinary speed with which the circus was erected soon gave rise to suggestions that the venture would be tainted by too much haste and too little attention to detail. But William Batty chose his architect wisely. Decades of experience erecting similar buildings in various parts of the United Kingdom paid hearty dividends. And his brief was simple. To combine substantiality (the most essential element of safety) with comfort and accommodation. The resulting structure is one of the biggest public buildings ever seen in Douglas. One hundred and twenty feet long and fifty feet wide, it can be seen for miles around. The exterior, though built of plain wooden timbers, is lavishly decorated with flags and banners and the entrance is hung with swags of colourful material, held in place by tasselled gold cords.

By the middle of June practically everything was in order for opening night. The weather was warm and dry and the performers, fresh from their latest engagement in Dublin, were settled in their lodgings. Unfortunately, high demand for shipping meant only seventeen of William Batty's valuable British, Hanoverian and Arabian horses and five diminutive piebald ponies arrived in time, with the final thirteen travelling separately a few days later. But this was no great obstacle to the launch of the season and great excitement greeted the posters and newspaper advertisements proclaiming the grand opening of Mr Batty's 'Evening Dreams of Wonder'.

Thanks to excellent planning and organised team work, the first night went like clockwork. The evening was a huge success, the critics were effusive in their praise and word quickly spread throughout the Island that Batty's Circus was not to be missed. William Batty, swiftly notified that all was well, was heartened that the Isle of Man promised to be the profitable venture he hoped for.

So it is that, after an opening week that's exceeded all expectations, the evening performance of Thursday the 29th of June is set to create a stir in Douglas, the like of which has never been seen before. For attending the circus will be the very highest echelons of Manx society led by the Queen's representative on the Island the Lieutenant Governor, His Excellency Major General John Ready and his wife Sarah, as well as many of the island's most respectable families.

The newspapers have done a sterling job in publicising the Governor's visit and consequently the Box Lobby at the circus has been busy all day. Every place in the boxes and pit sold out by mid-afternoon and the only tickets left are for a few spaces in the gallery for those willing to stand all night. The doors are due to open at seven o'clock and, as the appointed hour draws nearer, a great tide of humanity begins to swell the streets leading up to the circus. First to arrive are the gentry in a succession of carriages – General Younghusband, the Misses Hanby, Captains Webb and Servantes, the Reverend Read, Mrs Grantham and Mr Suckling amongst others. Behind them is another wave, on foot, led by Lawson the baker, Shimmin the grocer, Oates the confectioner, Manson the druggist, and Teare the butcher, scrubbed clean and dressed in their Sunday best.

As this lively gathering make their way through town they're joined by visitors who leave their lodgings dressed in their finest suits, gowns and bonnets, clutching fans to dispel the late June heat. Ascending the hill, the crowd grows with every corner passed until, by the time they reach Gick's Field, it has swollen to many hundreds of animated, noisy circus-goers. The evening is warm, with just the gentlest breeze, and as the circus building with its colourful banners comes into sight a rousing wave of music is carried across the balmy air. The circus band is seated by the entrance to the building and their trumpets, drums and flutes create an atmosphere of unbridled gaiety that incites the crowd to join in with their own singing as they wait to enter.

Nearly two decades have passed since Manx people were last treated to a circus and only a handful have a notion of what they may see inside the large wooden building. But even they take an audible breath as they pass from the lobby and bar into a vast, single room that dazzles with its brilliance. Every effort has been made to convey an atmosphere of luxury, gorgeousness, taste and elegance. This is no cheap, shoddy entertainment but a truly majestic space in which no expense has been spared.

From the moment the audience enter the auditorium through heavy, fringed, damask curtains they are immersed in a kaleidoscope of light and colour. Suspended from the ceiling, a huge, gas-powered crystal chandelier furnished with one hundred glowing burners casts an intense white light over the whole area. The air is full of dust motes and these catch the light reflected by the crystals, creating thousands of tiny rainbows which dance and sparkle. As each face in the crowd turns upward to gape at this marvel of engineering their eyes are also drawn to the vibrant, multi-hued lengths of American cotton which drape the entire ceiling. Gentle puffs of air blow in through vents in the roof causing the fabric to ripple and billow and the children in the audience tug on their parents' sleeves and point their fingers skyward, their eyes round with excitement.

All around the walls, a vivid palette of rich orpiment yellow, deep crimson lake, cobalt blue and emerald green has been used to create a flowing backdrop of alternating scenic and plain panels, framed with ornate patterns of gold, white and lemon. Interspersing the panels are decorative white columns entwined with perfectly painted climbing roses - a gentle contrast to the lifelike portraits of horses and wild beasts from William Batty's menagerie that are spaced around the arena. The result is a visual feast of opulence and foreign mysteries.

But it's not only the barrage of light, colour and exotic sights that thrill the crowd. Here, the entertainment will take place not upon a stage but in a ground-level circle that is covered with bright, white sawdust and surrounded by a four-foot high circular wooden barrier painted to resemble a stone wall, complete with tendrils of green ivy.

Alongside the circle, a dozen seats and music stands indicate the space reserved for the circus band, and a pit area next to the band, furnished with chairs and wooden benches, is quickly taken up by those spectators who've paid a shilling for their tickets. Those who can only afford sixpence are shepherded into a standing-only gallery behind the seats where they crush together, shoulder to shoulder. By contrast on the other side of the ring, with its own separate entrance, is a full tier of elaborately decorated and lavishly furnished side and dress boxes. Yet the marvel of this arrangement is that, whatever price has been paid by the ticketholder, the view of the arena is much the same whether seen from the comfort of a seat in the pit or boxes, or from a standing position in the gallery.

Out of sight, beyond the seating areas, are the performer's dressing rooms, a property room, harness room and the stalls for the horses which connect to the ring via wooden panelled corridors.

Over the next hour or so the auditorium gradually fills as the crowd settle into their places, and despite the vents in the ceiling the atmosphere becomes heavy with the smell of clammy bodies, warm ale, orange peel and a hundred gas lamps. Then, just before eight o'clock, the heavy curtains covering the entrance to the ring are pulled aside and a tall, imposing man enters the arena carrying a long, thin whip. Mr Thompson, the circus manager and conductor of the circle, is elegantly dressed in a long-tailed, black velvet riding jacket with satin lapels, cream riding breeches, high black boots with silver spurs, a cream silk shirt, patterned silk waistcoat and red silk cravat. His leathery face is adorned with finely trimmed sideburns, a waxed moustache and neat, pointed beard and his height is further accentuated by a black, burnished top hat.

Initially, Mr Thompson attempts to gain the crowd's attention by voice alone but when the chatter refuses to die down he resorts to a sudden, authoritative crack of his whip. At once, six hundred or so excited souls fall silent and he urges them to show their respect by standing for the arrival of His Excellency the Lieutenant Governor and his wife. As one body the audience rise to their feet and turn their eyes to the private box that has been especially fitted up for His Excellency's party. If the rest of the circus interior is agreeable, this box is positively luxurious in its trimmings - lined with green baize and hung with swathes of crimson velvet, furnished with soft, padded crimson chairs and decorated with intricate painted portraits of the company's star horses.

Mr Thompson now turns his attention to the band, instructing them to strike up 'God Save the Queen' and, with their hats clutched to their chests, the audience join together for a rousing version of the National Anthem. Once they've finished and the Governor is seated Mr Thompson bows to the Box, welcomes his honoured guests and invites them and the rest of the audience to make themselves comfortable in preparation for a varied and thrilling programme of equestrian feats and Olympian diversions.

It is not lost on Mr Thompson that this is the first evening in which all the boxes are completely full. While the gallery and pit have been well patronised during opening week, the town's elite have been remarkable by their absence. But tonight it seems that all of Douglas's most respectable citizens are here, in their finest costumes, hats and feathers. Lawyers, physicians, members of the high clergy and a number of guests from the Castle Mona Hotel have taken every good seat in the house and the ladies appear to have gone to no end of trouble with their outfits.

The evening begins in suitably glamorous style with an introductory set piece by star equestrian Selim Bridges, a mere youth of just seventeen years of age who rides with all the aplomb of a seasoned cavalry officer and has the bearing and confidence of someone twice his age (he also teaches the art of riding at the circus each morning, and drives the six-horse ceremonial coach that carries the circus band). This evening he astounds the audience - and the ladies in particular – with a dashing representation of many characters, dressed variously as a brigand chief, a Spanish Don, a fashionable dandy and most impressively, as Apollo on his winged steed. Heroism and chivalry pervade his every transformation and at one stage he has the audience in a swoon when he engages in a romantic scene with the noted equestrienne Miss O'Donnell - on temporary loan from Astley's – who plays an Italian flower girl, her hair spun with pink roses and her white gown adorned with colourful blooms.

Mr Bridges' ability to manage a galloping horse while leaping, jumping and throwing himself in all directions is truly breath-taking. But then, like so many circus equestrians, he was virtually born in the saddle. His parents had their own circus and a number of his equally gifted brothers and sisters are also performing here in Douglas, even the ten-year-old.

For the main part Selim Bridges is strikingly attired in red and gold military uniform, with black leather boots, tall black hat and a sword in a scabbard at his waist. But as he changes from one character to the next he variously adopts a range of costumes – from the swirling cloak and flamboyant collar of a Spanish adventurer, to the laurel wreath and skin-tight white tunic of a Greek God. Likewise, with every change of scene he is mounted on a different horse. A stunning, snorting, shiny black charger with full mane and tail is his chosen mount for the Spanish re-enactments, and a pure white, finely-boned mare, strapped with giant, life-like wings, for his mythical tales. In every scene his mounts are elaborately caparisoned in colourful coats of silken fabric, decorated with tassels, feathers and bejewelled harnesses. As the animals go through their movements, their rippling muscles and glossy manes gleaming under the lights, the audience are as much enchanted by them as their charismatic rider.

With each successive act the evening acquires an increasingly dream-like quality heightened by the warm colours that bathe each spectator, the magical glow of the chandelier and the comforting, earthy smell of horses and sawdust. In the Dress Boxes it appears to be considerably aided by the large quantities of champagne being consumed. Throughout the evening the audience glance frequently towards the Lieutenant Governor's party. He is an elderly man and quite frail, but he and his wife appear to be enjoying the performance immensely, laughing and applauding along with the crowd.

They seem particularly captivated by the drollery of the clever jester Henry Brown, who seamlessly fills the gaps between the equestrian scenes with his comic pantomimes. Mr Brown enters the arena in a series of somersaults and proceeds to berate the audience for their dress sense. This brings howls of laughter for he himself is dressed in a striking and most peculiar costume. His tight-fitting red and white pointed cap is divided by a red cockscomb and finished with small bells that tinkle every time he moves his head. His tunic is also half red and half white, vividly embroidered with leaves and gothic motifs, embellished on the cuffs with more bells and finished at the neck with a wide collar that's cut into deep points resembling a star. One of his legs is white, the other red, and his feet are encased in leather slippers with excessively long, pointed toes. Even his face presents something strange and somewhat alarming, smeared with thick white make-up accented by dark red lips, exaggerated laughter lines and pointed eyebrows. As he moves around the circle he gesticulates wildly with his jester's stick. To the young members of the audience this appears to be little more than a glorified infant's rattle, but sharp-eyed adults observe that it's decorated with both the head of a foolish ass and a wise owl – a pithy reference to the dichotomy of human nature.

Fortunately, Mr Brown's curious appearance is merely a foil to his razor-sharp wit and colourful comic oratory and he soon wins over the audience, at one point even playing to Mr Batty's most distinguished guests by delivering a clever, mock-electioneering speech of a Manx parliamentary candidate. Happily, this seems to highly amuse all levels of the audience and sets them in roars of laughter.

Halfway through the evening Mr Thompson informs the crowd of his great pleasure in introducing them to the famous 'fairy ponies'. To 'oohs' and 'aahs' and cries of glee, especially from the children, a group of tiny black and white ponies is led into the circle by their trainer Mr Bell. For the reward of a pat on the neck and a small edible treat secreted in Mr Bell's pocket they leap over poles and through hoops, fetch and carry, march and dance, wear cocked hats and cloaks, lace caps and mantles, and dine with the clowns on oaten pies. The audience are enthralled.

Finally, in deference to the honourable nature of tonight's audience, Mr Thompson announces that the evening will draw to a close with a Grand Masked Ball featuring the brightest stars of Mr Batty's stud.

With a great flourish the circus band launches into an energetic medley of waltzing and polka melodies. Selim Bridges leads his fellow equestrians into the circle, and with a booming command from Mr Thompson and a slicing crack of his whip, the circus arena explodes into a dizzying spectacle of colour and movement. For the next few minutes the crowd are transported as a dozen masked and spangled riders mounted on sleek chestnut horses trot in a series of elegant evolutions that are at once magical yet strangely familiar.

And then, just as dramatically as the evening began, it is suddenly all over. The performance has come to an unwelcome end and the audience rumble as though jolted from a dream. Mr Thompson swiftly moves in to request they stand for the departure of the Lieutenant Governor, but it seems the main party are also averse to leaving this temple of light and pleasure, loitering as they move from the box towards the exit. The still-dazed crowd follow them out of the building and jostle eagerly for position as His Excellency is helped into his waiting carriage. Although his bay horses are fine-looking animals the crowd can't help but compare them to the steeds they've just witnessed and find the comparison wanting.

It's dusk by the time the crowd reluctantly leaves Gick's Field, a vestige of warmth lingering in the air and half-light to help them through the murky streets. The sun has not long set behind the circus and the town and harbour laid out below are tinged with pink and gold.

Douglas has tonight experienced a truly wondrous evening that will linger long in the memory, especially for those in the audience returning home to tallow candles and dingy parlours. At this moment their spirits are on fire and their heads are filled with glorious images. It seems it isn't only the great halls of the British capital that will ensure William Batty full coffers and a place in history, but also a small island in the Irish Sea. His instincts were sound. Circus does indeed have a splendid future here.

Addendum

A month later, with their Manx season well underway, Batty's Circus held a benefit night for local charitable organisations. Proceeds from the evening went to the soup and medical dispensaries of Douglas, and the House of Industry.

In September the circus was disbanded and taken down. The timber and poles used in its construction were sold at auction to local builders.

In June 1851 William Batty opened a massive Hippodrome close to London's Crystal Palace. The venue, for equestrian displays, had covered seats and an open-air performance area. It was advertised as grander and bigger than anything ever attempted in England.

William Batty died on the 7th February 1868 at the age of sixty-seven and was buried in All Soul's Cemetery, Kensal Green in London. True to form even his funeral was a notable affair, described as exceptional, unique, tasteful and exceedingly appropriate. He died a wealthy man, leaving a fortune of nearly £80,000.

Chapter Five

THE SHOWMEN

1859 Friday 9th September

Douglas has today been shaken to its very foundations - and it all began in a most extraordinary manner.

At eleven o'clock this morning a tall young man dressed in an oversized brown coat, well-worn beaver hat, checked trousers and white Berlin gloves made his way noisily through the town's main streets, distributing colourful handbills and posters to shopkeepers from a large satchel slung over his shoulder. Passers-by openly stared at the young man, marked out by his bright green neckerchief and matching silk handkerchief poking brazenly from his breast pocket. If his dress and bold demeanour were not sufficient to brand him as a stranger in town, the impression was confirmed by his loud and frequent exhortations. For, as he bounded from one shop to another, he urged the good people of Douglas to lay down the tools of their trade at midday and look to the streets for a truly marvellous sight that would dazzle their eyes and fire their imaginations! Husbands should mind their wives and parents should mind their children, and if anyone failed to heed his words they would risk missing one of the greatest spectacles in the kingdom!

As the messenger forged a path through the crowded streets he was followed by another young man dressed in an eye-catching ensemble of patterned linen shirt and striped pantaloons, who tumbled and flip-flapped in his wake, drawing even more curious stares and startled comment. Inquisitive faces turned to the posters being pasted in shop windows and soon the streets were alight with the latest news of the circus currently visiting the Island. For this time, it seems the circus is not merely content for people to come to them. The circus is coming to the people.

To this effect, just before midday, a handful of police constables made their way along the Quay from the bottom of the Red Pier, up into Duke Street, left into the narrower confines of Drumgold Street and Great Nelson Street, up Great George Street, and finally along Athol Street to Gick's Field. Along the route they informed pedestrians, car men, boot-blacks and street traders that they would shortly need to clear the way to allow a circus procession to pass through. It seemed, however, that Douglas was not yet ready to abandon its daily business in favour of entertainers and showmen. Five minutes before noon, farmers were still to be seen driving their cattle through the streets, while rag-and-bone men whipped up their tired nags drawing carts piled high with old linen, tattered vestments and animal bones.

Even in the smart shopping strand of Duke Street, fashionable townsfolk whose business was less pressing failed to heed the warnings immediately. But then, as clocks all over town struck twelve, the strains of distant music could be heard emanating from down near the Quay. Gradually the music grew louder, drowning out the urban background of chatter and commerce. Heads began to turn and without any further urging the crowds fell away to the sides of the street, leaving a wide space down the middle. Soon the upper windows of every building were filled with heads poking out, all eager to see what was going on. Small boys scrambled onto high walls and window ledges, and benevolent fathers hoisted pleading youngsters onto their shoulders. And then it came. An unnerving tremor underfoot and a rumble like distant thunder that made the hairs rise on the back of the neck. All eyes now focussed in the direction of the Quay and a ripple of excitement coursed through the waiting assembly.

As the air filled with the sound of trumpets, cymbals, piccolos, violins and the boom of a big bass drum, the circus parade came into view. And what a sight it was. Eight handsome, gleaming horses harnessed two abreast in four rows of matching pairs, turned into the street, their hooves clattering harshly on the cobbles. With bridles jingling, brasses glinting and red plumes shaking between their pricked-up ears, they progressed steadily forward, an enormous triumphal bandwagon trundling heavily behind them on gaily-painted wheels, trims singing as metal struck stone. The sides of the wagon were clearly emblazoned with the words 'Ginnett's Royal Hippodrome' writ large in red letters with gilded edges, and the driver of the wagon, no less than Mr Frederick Ginnett himself, cut an eye-catching figure. Sitting high up on the whip's bench, attired in a blue coat, white waistcoat and cravat and black top hat, he led the parade with all the confidence of a man who has the world at his feet. Thoroughly at ease with the challenge of negotiating an eight-horse coach through sloping, uneven streets, here was a man totally at one with his charges, steering them with lively vocal commands and such deft handling of the reins that he was even able to doff his hat to the crowd in response to their cheers and hollers.

The people of Douglas were agog. Although at times the horses and wagon wheels passed by only inches from their feet, they still elbowed and shoved one another to peer even closer at this fantastical parade. The wagon itself was probably ten or more feet high, painted in red and white, extravagantly embellished with swirling, gilded wooden carvings. Strung from each corner were flags in the blue, red and white colours of France (according to the handbills, Frederick's father Jean Pierre – the Ginnett Circus founder - came to England as a prisoner of war after Waterloo). Even the spokes of the wheels, painted in rosettes of bright red, yellow and white, created an eye-catching burst of colour and movement as the wheels revolved.

Seated directly behind Mr Ginnett, the circus band produced its own gay union of sound and colour. Six in number, they sat on parallel benches that ran along the top of the wagon – easily as high as the tallest shop windows – dressed in peaked military caps and belted, buckled uniforms, trimmed with lustrous brass buttons and gold braid that flashed in the sun. Their instruments shone from hours of polishing and the music they played was as lively and spirited as a dawn chorus on a late summer morning.

But the band was simply an entrée for the remainder of the parade. Following behind the main wagon a dozen or more lavishly-costumed male and female riders trotted along in lively fashion, mounted on a mix of cream Arab horses and spotted ponies caparisoned in coloured bridles and saddle cloths. Spectators waving and calling out to the riders were amply rewarded with flowers and oranges thrown their way, and as they pushed back to make room for the circus artistes it appeared to those looking down from above as though a bright bejewelled ribbon was being stitched into a length of grey woollen cloth.

Behind the equestrians a small, flat-bed wagon carried a tiny pony wearing a placard round its neck proclaiming it to be 'the smallest pony in the world – just 25 inches high!' At every bump in the road the pony showed the whites of its eyes and the onlookers gushed with sentiment. Finally, bringing up the rear, half a dozen youthful male riders brandishing rifles and looking quite the part in red military uniforms, re-enacted the Battle of the Alma as they made their way through the narrow streets of Douglas, much to the delight – if not full comprehension - of young boys who watched open-mouthed from their cramped vantage points.

By half past twelve the parade had passed through the lower part of town, with only the occasional hiatus prompted by the need to manoeuvre eight horses and a large wagon around some especially tight corners. The lead wagon also adopted a noticeably slower pace along

Great Nelson Street, drawing the crowd's attention to the attractive circus posters hung in the windows of Mrs Davidson's house, the lodgings of Mr and Mrs Ginnett for the duration of their season. Mrs Davidson will naturally be in receipt of the best seats in the house for her trouble.

Turning finally into Athol Street, on the town's fashionable upper perimeter, the circus procession could finally breathe again. Aside from Duke Street, old Douglas is a pungent, cramped and dirty maze of rough road surfaces potted with ruts and holes. Athol Street presented Mr Ginnett's entourage with another world, its long, straight road surface smoothly paved with tarmacadam, and its fine buildings home to the town's police station and courthouse, as well as a number of respectable lodging houses and genteel private residences of surgeons, architects and attorneys. Here the circus procession could enjoy the sort of welcome they felt they deserved.

As the parade slowed for the final push up hill to Gick's Field, the band dismounted from the lead wagon and walked alongside the horses as they made their way to the circus ground. A large swell of townsfolk had followed them up the hill and once the landscape began to flatten off they gained their first thrilling sight of Ginnett's Grand Pavilion. If the parade presented a memorable first for the Island, this marvellous auditorium presented another. Where William Batty's grand building once stood over a decade ago there now stands a huge circular canvas marquee, one hundred feet in diameter, topped with flags and banners and secured to the ground by vast lengths of thick rope.

The advance agents urged the crowd to 'walk up, walk up' as they approached the marquee, informing them with practised enthusiasm that, within, there is space for nearly two and half thousand people. Four hundred first class seats, a thousand second class and a thousand third class, with prices ranging from just sixpence to two shillings for the grandest boxes. The company are putting on two shows a day during their stay in the Isle of Man and the whole arena is brilliantly illuminated by lamps lit with portable gas. If the people of the Isle of Man would be kind enough to bestow their patronage on Mr Ginnett this evening, the agents were confident that nothing that has ever been seen on the Isle of Man before will bear the slightest comparison!

And by this evening it seems that the agents – and the parade – have done a fine job. The audience drawn to Gick's Field to enjoy tonight's performance is staggering in its proportions, equivalent to a sixth of the entire population of Douglas. There's even a large party of pleasure trippers who've journeyed by the steamer 'Manx Fairy' from Ramsey in order to be here. Every available seat around the central sawdust circle is taken, tightly crammed with bodies swaddled in thick suits, hats, gloves and the full fashions of the season, yet the sound of voices, music and laughter fills the marquee as they wait in the warm half-light beneath the canvas roof.

They could have chosen to visit a play or recital for their evening's entertainment – but why sit in gloom when this marvellous hippodrome offers so much more?

Following an afternoon of performance, rest, rehearsal and attention to horses and costumes, the company are preparing to exert themselves once again. Or, as the posters would have it, provide an exhibition of swift, rapid and daring horsemanship, gymnastics of every form and fashion, miraculous feats never seen before in this town, all executed with skill and perfection - in fact, The Greatest Combination of Talent ever concentrated within the walls of any Cirque, Ancient or Modern!

Not everyone is happy, however. Behind the scenes, Mr Ginnett's star performer, the world-renowned American equestrienne Ella, has become tiresome with her demands. Or at least, her manager's demands have become tiresome. When not in the circle, Ella herself maintains a clear distance from the other artistes and is rarely heard to converse with anyone other than her manager Spencer Stokes and her female chaperone. But Mr Stokes does a fine job of speaking for her. Firstly, he requested a corner of the female dressing room to be cordoned off with a screen, 'for added security and privacy'. Then it was a separate loose box for Ella's Arab mare Zaidee to be fed and groomed by her own personal groom. Then it was a range of samplers and embroidery threads to be supplied, so that 'the world-renowned Ella' could be kept from boredom during intervals. If it wasn't for the fact that Ella is drawing in the multitudes, Mr Ginnett would be curtailing her services forthwith.

But Mr Ginnett is well aware that Ella is no ordinary equestrian. The darling of Europe for the past eight years, a star in Berlin, St Petersburgh, London and Paris, she has wooed the general public with her exciting, New World riding style. And with her sweet face and graceful bearing she's also allegedly wooed a number of Continental dukes and nobles, the Arab mare being just one of the many extravagant gifts pressed on her by wealthy admirers. Even at today's parade it was clear from the whistles and shouting that she'd instantly captured the hearts of the young men of Douglas. Tonight, she has the lead billing and Mr Ginnett has asked the town police to be on hand should there be any rough behaviour amongst the infatuated lotharios who tend to swarm in her presence.

Then there are the problems surrounding another headline act. Chevalier Houri – the Fire King or 'living Salamander' – has taken his inspiration from another, more famous, Fire King performing in London in recent years. But he isn't always as successful as his namesake and Frederick Ginnett is concerned that the Chevalier may harm not only himself but members of the public. His bold display is to conclude tonight's show and all circus hands have been asked to stand by with buckets of water should things go wrong.

Fortunately, the other members of the company are less troublesome and bring years of experience to the arena. Madame Amelia was the principal artiste at the Grand Cirque in Vienna, John Samwells is regarded as England's premier horseman, young Lloyd rides his horse 'Firefly' bare-back with great poise, and the Elliott family of gymnasts are as tight a group of performers as you could wish for. And then there is the ever-popular pantomime of 'Dick Turpin' – but Frederick Ginnett himself takes the role of Dick and he and his horse have performed it countless times together to great acclaim.

It is nineteen-year-old Ella, though, the fearless and beautiful equestrienne from across the ocean, who the audience have really come to see. In her dressing room there have been tantrums, harsh words and throwing of gloves, but as Mr Stokes helps her to mount her mare, Ella is a picture of composure. She enters the circle to a roar of approval. The young farmers in the third-class seats elbow one another for the best view of horse and rider, while the bachelors in first-class wave their handkerchiefs at the flying apparition who now boldly dashes around the sawdust.

There is no doubt Ella presents a picture of pure loveliness. Her parents were Creole, the exotic French heritage of Louisiana, and her face is strikingly beautiful, with regular, delicate features; large, dark eyes, shapely brows and smooth olive skin, flushed with a rosy glow. She is dressed in a light, floating, knee-length gown cinched at her slender waist by a wide sash and layered over a silk petticoat that flies behind her. The short-sleeved bodice of the gown has a high neck and is trimmed with ruffles of white lace. On her arms she wears cream satin elbow-length gloves and pearl bracelets and her shapely legs are encased in cream silk tights with soft leather pumps on her feet. Her raven black hair, which normally hangs in luxuriant curls to her waist, is tonight gathered around her head in a braid and crowned with a circle of silk flowers.

Those members of the audience who are interested in the appearance of Ella's Arab mare are equally satisfied. The horse has been carefully groomed and its coat and long flowing mane and tail shine under the gas lamps. Red and gold braid adorn its bridle, and its back is draped with a long red seat pad covered with elaborate embroidery and finished with a deep gold trim, secured around its chest and belly with wide red and gold webbing.

Ella does not have the circle to herself, however. Directing the action is Mr Ginnett who stands in the centre of the ring, whip in hand, alongside a couple of clowns and two musicians playing flutes. On top of the circle wall there are also four young men, each stationed next to one of the thick timber posts which support the marquee's canvas roof.

After a few circuits of the sawdust Ella has established her horse's pace and stride and she rises up to a crouching position on its back. At a signal from Mr Ginnett each of the men standing on the wall produces a large, flower-covered hoop and leans in towards the circle, clinging onto the timber posts with one arm and using the other to stretch his hoop out over the sawdust. As her mare canters steadily around the ring Ella leaps through each hoop, landing lightly on the back of her horse with perfect precision. The crowd go wild with excitement as she proceeds to complete five full rounds of the circle with barely a swerve or quiver (and even those moments merely add to the sense of exhilaration in the tent). Her control of her horse is astonishing and her balance and self-assurance awe inspiring.

Her next feat follows a similar vein but this time the young men stretch broad strips of calico across the circle, above the height of her horse's head. Urging her mount to a full gallop she proceeds to leap over the calico, apparently springing from and alighting on her knees. This is not only impressive in itself but the calico is held so closely together that she hardly has time to pause between leaps.

It's her next exhibition, however, that truly raises the bar and has the audience jabbering like canaries. After an absence from the ring of five minutes in which the clowns take over, she returns - riding bare-back. Such brazen performance by a female equestrian is unheard of here and the audience is clearly divided in their consideration of this new American art. There's even a slight commotion as some members of the audience show their disapproval by making for the exit. But those who stay are treated to a virtuoso display of control and equilibrium beyond anything they've seen before. Riding her horse around and across the circle at speed, Ella faces forward, then backwards, then sideways, then lies across her horse's back before finally facing forward again for three full circles, allowing her to wave adieu to her adoring admirers. Raucous shouts of 'bravo!' from first class and 'hurrah' from the rear follow her as she disappears into the dark recesses of the horse corridor, continuing long after Mr Stokes has pulled the curtain across and whisked her away to her dressing room.

The rest of the evening proceeds in a similarly exhilarating manner. The remainder of Mr Ginnett's company are adept, well-rehearsed performers and the Grand Pavilion hums with the sound of satisfied customers. To round off the evening's indoor entertainment the company stage the celebrated story of 'Dick Turpin's Ride to York' or 'The Death of Black Bess', a dramatic piece that offers everything a hungry audience could wish for. Frederick Ginnett relishes playing the role of the legendary eighteenth-century highwayman and enters the circle on his rearing black charger, brandishing a pistol in the air, his face concealed beneath a black scarf. Against a background of shouting, pistol shots and general pandemonium the enthralled audience then witness a high-speed, potted version of the old tale that takes them from the attempted robbery of a stagecoach packed with passengers to the shooting of Tom King at Spaniard's Tavern and Turpin's pursuit by the Bow Street Runners. It's an exhausting, colourful, chaotic farce, full of dark comedy and gymnastic tumbling and the audience love every minute. Only when Turpin is supposedly within sight of York and his faithful mount collapses from exhaustion – a scene movingly re-enacted by Ginnett and his horse - do they fall silent. When the Runners catch up with Turpin and drag him off to the gallows two thousand circus-goers roar their dismay and stamp their feet.

At any other time Frederick Ginnett would have considered this a suitable point to bid his audience farewell and conclude the entertainments. But not so this evening. They still have one more thrill in store. Ushering the giant crowd to the marquee's exits he announces that if they would be so kind as to step outside into Gick's

Field they will witness a demonstration at once both enthralling and edifying.

Making their way out of the tent the audience are regaled by a short, bearded fellow offering small publications of his booklet 'The Life and Art History of Miss Ella's by Spencer Stokes'. Those with spare loose change take a copy but their attention is already elsewhere. For in the middle of Gick's Field, a few hundred yards downwind from the canvas pavilion, they are being directed to a strange structure. It is dark over Douglas now, the only illumination a dull glow from inside the canvas tent and torches stuck into the ground along the pathways, and the crowd can vaguely discern a large metal frame, similar to a garden arbour, made of two intersecting tunnels that form the shape of a cross. The arbour is loosely covered with twigs, sticks, gorse and brushwood and the four entrances into the structure, as tall as a man, have been left clear. The crowd scuttle forward to investigate further, but are kept back by circus hands who urge them to keep their distance. All will be revealed soon enough.

It is left to Mr Ginnett to once again direct the action. Stepping in front of the crowd he begs their silence and asks that they set all rational thinking to one side for the next few minutes. Children must be closely watched and all due care given to safety for what they are about to see defies the very laws of nature! With that he moves aside and, in his place, appears a terrifying sight. At first glance the figure that emerges from the darkness appears to be a ghoulish, faceless monster, covered head to toe in a thick, shapeless canvas garment somewhat similar to that of a submarine diver, which totally encloses his hands and feet. The garment is smeared with a reddish-white slime and the creature's face is obscured by a mask completely devoid of features other than two 'eyes' made of thin horn. The crowd is stunned into silence and some youngsters cry with fear.

But then a man moves toward the apparition and removes what is revealed to be a canvas helmet from his head. Now able to speak and breathe, the 'creature' announces that he is none other than the Chevalier Houri, the great Fire King and only living Salamander, who will shortly demonstrate a charmed life as he walks amid leaping flames and destructive fire. With that, a number of young men bearing torches move towards the iron cage and set light to the brush, which catches quickly and soon creates a raging inferno. When the flames are at their highest, soaring ten to twenty feet in the air, the Chevalier is once again helped to don his helmet and without any hesitation he enters the arbour and calmly walks through the intense fire, appearing on the other side apparently unaffected and with his clothing perfectly intact. He then repeats the feat several times, appearing at different exits each time to show there's no trickery involved. By this time the ferocity of the flames has forced the crowd to move thirty feet away but they're still able to distinguish his bulky shape moving around the frame and the air is filled with cries of anguish and disbelief.

At last the flames die down and the Chevalier is able to remove his hideous suit. Clouds of steam billow from his helmet as it's removed and it appears to bulge alarmingly. His hair is plastered to his head and rivulets of perspiration stream down his face. Miraculously, however, his limbs are completely unharmed and the only visible ill-effects are a reddened complexion and husky voice. And it's in these gravelly, broken tones that he confides to his astonished audience that, for the price of a minor discomfort, he is confident his unique garment would allow a person to survive in a burning building for at least a good ten minutes. With that in mind, he hopes it will soon be considered by all fire brigades for the preservation of life.

On which extraordinary note the evening performance of Ginnett's Royal Hippodrome finally comes to an end and the vast assembly begins to disperse. Though the heavens are not done with them yet. Even as town and country folk make their way home, and trippers return to their waiting steamer, a sublime celestial display is playing out a memorable encore in the skies above Douglas. Brilliant flashes of green and violet light follow one another across the dark sky with great rapidity. Coloured swirls and streaks sway and dance high above the earth. In days to come it will be reported that these strange and beautiful illuminations are the Aurora Borealis, the mesmerising Northern Lights. They have certainly provided an unexpected finale to a remarkable day. Frederick Ginnett could not have arranged it better himself.

Addendum

The following week Ginnett's advertised that they would not be visiting any other town on the island but Douglas. Just five days later they published details of an extensive tour round the Isle of Man featuring visits to Castletown, Peel, Kirk Michael, Ramsey, Laxey and Douglas!

In 1860 newspapers in York reported a planned appearance in the city by Fire King, the Chevalier Houri. Unfortunately, he never had the chance to impress the public as his posters attracted a gang of boys who set fire to his equipment and chased him round the field.

Only a few months after thrilling the crowds on the Isle of Man with 'her' fearless riding Ella the American equestrienne was revealed to be a man by the real name of Omar Kingsley. Kingsley had been taken in by Spencer Stokes at a very young age, trained in horse riding and, because of his attractive looks, was dressed as a girl. However, by the age of sixteen, Kingsley began to rebel against this double life and insisted on being able to wear men's clothing away from the ring. He went on to perform to great acclaim around the world, as both a male and female persona, and died of smallpox while appearing in India in the late 1870s.

Frederick Ginnett passed away at his home in Brighton in January 1892 after a bout of influenza. He had enjoyed a lifelong career in the circus, having made his first public appearance in Brighton at the age of six before King William IV. At the time of his death he was praised for understanding the tastes and wants of the public better than any other circus proprietor in the United Kingdom.

He owned a circus in Brighton and over the years had also built permanent circuses at Portsmouth, Belfast, Torquay, Plymouth and Cork.

Chapter Six

THE WIRE WALKER

1861 Thursday 8th August

The nom-de-plume was the idea of the advance agent. You have to have a draw, he said. A hook, a pull, a tease, a taste. A dab of excitement on the tongue to lure the children. A scent of danger in the nose to tempt the adults. Something so bold that it will set your circus aside from all the others. Yes, you have good horses, he said, and daring riders and clever clowns. But you need something truly breath-taking if you are to convince the people of Douglas to part with their hard-earned shillings. And if there's one name that stirs up a fever of anticipation like no other it is surely that of Blondin. Why, it's hard to read a newspaper these days without seeing mention of the brave little Frenchman and his daring crossings of the Niagara Falls and high wire exploits at Crystal Palace.

In England, said the agent, it seems that every other tight rope artiste, whether male or female, has taken to modelling themselves on Blondin. So, does it not make sense that your artiste should follow suit? After all, she is well versed in performing the very stunts for which he's famous, and you can guarantee the chance to see an audacious young girl smiling in the face of death will have the people of Douglas fighting for the best view!

It's now a week since that conversation took place. At the time The Powell Brother's circus was still otherwise engaged at the Zoological Gardens in Liverpool – and their tightrope artiste Madame Zepha Davies was enjoying a highly successful season. Today, however, it is not 'Madame Davies' who will appear before a salivating public on a windswept Douglas hillside but the daring, the bold, the extraordinary 'Madam Blondin'. And it seems the new appellation has already proved its worth. Word has spread through Douglas like wildfire that not only is she going to perform feats that defy all imagination, but her outdoor performance will be un-ticketed. The town is packed with visitors and they can't believe their luck to have such free entertainment laid at their feet.

The circus company arrived two days ago on the Steam Packet's mail boat from Liverpool, a calm and pleasant journey that allowed for six valuable hours of much needed rest. As the company won't be on Manx soil long enough to justify a wooden building they brought their own giant marquee with them and the hiatus at sea was a particular boon for the tent riggers and canvas men who've since been toiling virtually without a break.

When it came to off-loading, the ton weight of canvas rolls, poles, iron stakes, ropes, cables, cranks and pulleys filled a number of wagons, requiring considerable horse and man power to haul them up to the southern end of Gick's Field. There the wagons halted on a level stretch of grass adjoining the main road to Peel, facing 'The Brown

Bobby', a former coaching inn that used to mark the divide where town ended and countryside began. Nowadays, the old inn is encroached upon by new terraced houses that creep ever closer, and the new Circular Road which links the main roads to the west and the north of the Island. But this is all good news for the Powell brothers. The chosen site has put the circus close to some of the Island's largest gentrified properties and it's on the periphery of a constantly busy junction. Day and night the roads in this part of town are filled with carriages, their seats lined with satin, their passengers plump with banknotes.

Not that everything is going in the company's favour. Although the air is still very warm, the town's been buffeted by a strong wind over the last two days, challenging the large team of men putting up the tent.

Wielding hefty sledgehammers with a steady, practised, musical cadence they began by driving metal stakes into the ground in a large circle, every strike singing across the field like church bells as the men heaved and grunted, the warm wind carrying the sound of their labours and flicking sweat into their eyes. As they worked dozens of other men swarmed around the field like worker ants. Thick rolls of roof canvas were dragged into the circle and set down at regular spaces; bundles of side poles were mathematically placed in readiness around the circumference of the tent; and the giant centre pole, a forty foot long trunk of tapering timber, was carried into the centre and carefully laid down with its widest end adjacent to a large hole in the ground, dug especially for the purpose.

With a great deal of noise and effort the pole was gradually raised into the air, the men straining against the wind, and once its ropes were secured, a wave of cheers and clapping broke out while some of the younger lads grappled each other to the ground, laughing and scuffling in the dirt until the tent master called them to order.

Soon it was time for the roof canvas to be unfurled and each section laced together. The canvas bucked and danced in the wind but the riggers, many of them ex-seamen, worked methodically and with surprising speed, their time handling sails evident in their finely tuned rhythm. Alongside them, hired locals grunted and groaned in their attempts to keep pace, their fingers clumsy and their palms raw.

Once the canvas was ready, half a dozen well-muscled fellows began to pull the roof upwards, aided by two heavy horses. By the time the canvas finally rose majestically into the air the light was fading and, once it had been properly secured, the tent master called for 'down tools'. Work would resume at four in the morning.

For the next few hours most of the workers slept beneath the canvas roof, wrapped in rough blankets. When the wake-up call came torches were lit and small fires sprang into life around the edges of the field, their flames leaping in the wind. As the sky mellowed from midnight black to daybreak purple the whole scene took on the guise of some strange drama, bulky shadows criss-crossing back and forth against a backdrop of bright orange flares.

First task of the new day was to hook the smaller rolls of side canvas onto the edges of the roof, unroll them like theatre curtains and lace them together, pegging them firmly into the ground to prevent canny youngsters from creeping in without paying. Then all hands were mustered to dress the entrance with signs and placards. Only then was it possible to set the stage for the Powell brother's most enticing drawcard – Madam Blondin's ascension of a tightrope on the outside of the tent.

Zepha and her husband Robert – clown, acrobat, equestrian and all-round 'useful man' – personally supervised the rigging of the wire. Recent tales of accidents caused by old or rotten hemp rope have persuaded her to use one-and-a-half inch steel hawser wire instead. It may be more costly than rope but is certainly less costly than broken bones.

With one end already secured to the top of the centre pole, the remainder was reeled out across the grassy meadow in the half-darkness to a copse of small trees at the edge of the field, allowing for an angle of approximately thirty degrees. After cranking to create the correct tension two long cavaletti ropes were attached to the wire and pegged into the ground on either side and three shorter ballast ropes tied on and hung with heavy sandbags. Zepha then hopped up onto the wire and nimbly walked a few paces, twisting and turning and fluttering her arms until satisfied that all was well.

At six o'clock all activity on the field was halted to allow for breakfast. Pots were slung over the fires and water boiled while the younger members of the Powell company were sent down to the Quay with orders for bread, dripping, oatmeal and herrings. Everyone was ravenous and the meal was conducted in silence.

By the time they'd finished the sun was high in the sky and groups of curious locals appeared around the edges of Gick's Field to watch in fascination as the circus came alive. From a distance the finished tent appeared to be a handsome construction, a giant, off-white canvas 'cake', rimmed with a coloured frill that rippled in the wind. On all sides hundreds of guy ropes strained and creaked as the tent moved and shuddered. On the northern aspect, facing away from the wind, the entrance and striped ticket booth stood ready to welcome in the audience with garish painted placards of horses, acrobats and clowns and a large colourful painted sign announcing the establishment of "Powell's Circus Royal" and their company of renowned British and Contintental Artistes.

The rest of the morning passed in a flurry of activity. Men, women and children ducked in and out of the painted wagons parked around the edge of the field, laden with costumes and harnesses. Horses and ponies stood tethered under the trees, flicking their tails as grooms brushed the dust out of their patchwork coats. Inside the tent, long benches were laid out and carpets rolled and sawdust raked. By midday Gick's Field resembled a colourful pantomime, the set dressed, the cast primped and preened, the band waiting in the wings.

The size of the company means they've had neither the time nor money to spend on lavish street parades, but the site is in a prime spot and the Powell brothers are counting on the Blondin name to work its magic. According to their advance agent, only last month the people of the Isle of Man flocked to see a painting portraying Blondin crossing the Niagara Falls and in the newspapers his exploits on the high wire still fill inches of column space. If it's not Blondin 'with eyes bandaged' it is Blondin 'turns a somersault' or even Blondin 'cooks an omelette'! It's hard to believe in fact that, when he first appeared, this darling of two continents was widely considered to be a fake. If Zepha Davies can match his feats by even half she will have earned her money well.

Madam Blondin's outdoor performance is due to begin at two. At one the field was cleared and within minutes the first spectators arrived, their voices carrying over the hillside. They are a northern lot mostly, holidaymakers from England's industrial heartland, come to the Island for a change of air and entertaining distractions. In the warmth of this August day they are likely to satisfy both, but in larger measure than they could ever have anticipated.

The wire draws them towards the field like a lure. The wind is making it hum, an eerie, keening sound that draws the hairs on the back of the neck. The spectators line the edge of the field, clambering onto walls and trees for the best vantage point. And not only to watch Madam Blondin. For the Powells have chanced upon a spectacular setting. From here the viewer looks down towards the Hills Meadow and valley of the River Dhoo as it meanders towards Douglas harbour, then up the other side of the valley to the green pastures of Carnane hill. To the east, it is just possible to make out the masts of ships lined up in the harbour, while to the west is the ancient estate of the Nunnery in its glorious wooded setting.

By two o'clock the southern end of Gick's Field is bursting at the seams. A thousand holidaymakers stand shoulder to shoulder, all craning their necks to catch a first glimpse of 'Madam Blondin'. The wind is still whipping across the hillside and ladies clutch their bonnets as they wait, the flapping of the tent drowning out any attempts at delicate conversation. And then, suddenly, she is before them, a young woman of just nineteen years, escorted through the throng to the base of the wire by a man dressed in a frilled white tunic, white pantaloons and white stockings. His face is completely white, accented with painted red lips and eyes and he wears a small conical hat on his head. As she sits at the base of the wire to complete her last-minute preparations the young woman gives the clown a warm smile, to which he replies by bowing and producing an egg from behind his left ear.

The crowd are still laughing as John Powell steps forward. Madam Blondin, he announces, is possibly the premier tightrope artiste in the whole of Britain, engaged by Powell's Great British and Continental Circus at great expense. Today she will not only ascend the full length of this wire to the very top of Powell's Grand Circus pavilion but anyone who purchases a ticket for tonight's show will witness her perform feats on the indoor high wire that can easily rival the real Blondin!

With every word the crowd push even further forward. Many of them have started their day in nearby taverns and, while most are in jovial mood, a good portion make no disguise that they are simply here to court danger. Many even hope she will fall. A ghoulish few take bets on it. And their money could be safe, for in this wind, 'Madam Blondin' will need all her wits about her if she's to reach the centre pole and make a safe return.

Fortunately for Zepha Davies, what the crowd do not know is that she has been dancing on a tightrope since infancy. Ever since she first learnt to balance on a moving ball while holding her parents' hands she has practised, practised, practised. In fact, practise is now as habitual and necessary to her as breathing because "miss one day" as the old folks say "and one day your feet may miss". Quite simply, when not performing she is rehearsing, and when not rehearsing she is performing. Prior to coming to the Isle of Man she and Robert worked their way tirelessly through dozens of towns in the north of England and this short contract as 'Madam Blondin' gives her the chance to develop her act further. Which gives her an undeniable thrill. For a sense of danger is not merely a side element of a good tightrope performance – it is essential, and with the name Blondin comes increased risk. And bigger risk means more money.

As Zepha arrived on the field her small frame was draped in a dark blue mantle, showing only her hair, neatly parted in the middle and gathered into braided clusters on either side of her head. But the mantle is now discarded, allowing the audience to gape at her skimpy costume - a sleeveless satin doublet that flashes with spangles; padded trunk hose, and pale pink fleshings that cover her legs yet suggest the appearance of naked skin. Her chest and arms are brazenly bare. She's not very tall but her body is straight and toned, her muscles well-defined, with a firm, rounded backside and heavy, solid thighs. Her appearance is at once provocative, outrageous and highly erotic.

Before she can begin her ascension Zepha stretches her limbs, bending and pulling her arms and legs and rotating her ankles. The warm-up is necessary for the success of her performance but she can't help playing to the men who ogle her as though she is a dancer in a Parisian saloon. On her feet she's wearing soft, well-patched, leather boots with thin suede soles and she takes a lingering moment to rub rosin into the soles to help her grip the wire, all the time aware of the eyes fixed upon her shapely legs.

When she's completed her preparations, Robert, in his clown costume, helps her up onto the wire and urges the crowd to stand well back as she's handed her balancing pole. The pole is thirty feet long and flexes, drooping lower at both ends. The wind catches it and for a second Zepha grips it hard to stop it flying out of her hands. Then, a small bow to the audience signals that she's ready to begin walking. A pistol is fired, the crowd fall silent and she places her right foot forward.

With her chin up, eyes fixed on the distant roof, legs slightly bent and back ramrod straight, she moves confidently in small, measured steps, taking her weight on the balls of her feet. Each step is a single, fluid movement, sliding the soft sole of her boot onto the wire and deftly placing the heel of each foot so that it touches the toes of the one behind. To maintain her balance she holds the balancing pole at waist height, her hands just wide of her hips, keeping the centre of her body directly over the wire. As she rises higher above the ground she soon draws level with the heads of the crowd and young men lurch forward to get a closer view of her wondrous, near-naked arms and legs. But the majority of the audience simply hold their breath, fixated by her grace and daring. Her limbs are as supple as a cat, yet she seems to have the strength and backbone of a lion.

The force of the wind has the crowd hanging onto their hats and voluminous crinolines and it soon becomes evident that 'Madam Blondin' may struggle against the elements. The wire is swaying slightly, despite the sandbags and guy rope, and, worse still, it is rotating beneath her feet. No one can see this but she feels it through the soles of her boots. She grips the pole harder to retain her balance and continues to move forward at a steady pace. Remarkably, her face shows no fear, only an intense concentration. Her gaze is absorbed, trance-like; focus and determination etched into every muscle.

By the time she's halfway up the wire the crowd has become impatient, shoving forward to stand beneath her, despite the effort of the circus hands to keep them back. Some men, the worse for drink, call out with lurid suggestions but they're shouted down. One or two are dragged away, arms flailing and obscenities trailing behind them. Consequently, they're not around when 'Madam Blondin' misses a beat. It's a particularly sharp gust that has caught her off-balance. The crowd fall silent, sick with apprehension, as she wobbles, pauses, and slowly goes down on one knee, breathing deeply. Within seconds the moment has passed, she regains her composure, stands straight and proceeds steadily up the second half of the wire. The spectators applaud loudly. This is definitely not for the squeamish.

Once she is walking above the tent roof Zepha appears to be more assured and quickens her pace, pushing against the flurries of warm air that assail her from every angle. As she makes the summit and grabs onto the top of the centre pole, she turns and waves down to the vast sea of ant-like bodies that stretches out across the field as far as the eye can see. In return, they roar with appreciation. Within the crowd a dozen circus men take advantage of their enthusiastic reaction to 'do a mob', pushing their way through with empty hats extended to gather the notes and coin being generously tossed in the heat of the moment.

Zepha's downward walk is similarly tense but thankfully uneventful and when she finally reaches the security of solid ground the crowd breaks into hearty, prolonged applause, spiked with cheers and wolf whistles that are swept around the hillside. An especially ardent group chant 'Ma-dam Blon-din, Ma-dam Blon-din' over and over, an infectious refrain that on any other occasion would delight Zepha Davies. But today it barely registers. The ascension has been unusually taxing and has taken its toll, mentally and physically. Her skin is filmed with sweat, her face pale and clammy. For many minutes she's too tense to speak and squeezes her eyes shut in an effort to blank out the jabbering cacophony of voices that surrounds her. Pushing the melee aside, her husband, the clown, carefully wraps her in her mantle and gently ushers her through the press of bodies to their wagon and a hot cup of tea. Tonight, she will perform to a ticketed audience. The stakes will be higher. She needs her rest.

The afternoon passes in a blur of rehearsal and mundane chores. Torn seams and hems are mended, tights washed and darned, boots buffed. Inside the tent the rig for the high wire is set up and checked over and rehearsal is taken in snatches between circling horses and fooling clowns. To the outsider it appears to be a chaotic scene, filled with noise and movement. There is no time to prepare a proper meal and late in the day Zepha and Robert share a bundle of bread, cheese and radishes on a small platform twenty-five feet above the ground.

In the evening, the circus fills up quickly with all the good and great of Douglas, a large group of military men in full uniform, and hundreds of visitors – the men in summer tweeds, the women in Indian shawls, hooded cloaks, wide, flounced skirts and heavily trimmed bonnets. The equestrian acts go down well and the audience are effusive in their appreciation but there's only one act they really want to see.

At nine o'clock, halfway through the evening, it's announced that 'Madam Blondin' is to perform her extraordinary feats upon the high wire and a hush falls over the crowd as a small figure skips into the ring and nimbly scampers up a narrow ladder to the platform, accompanied by drum rolls from the band. For a minute or two, she styles, posing and bowing to the sea of faces and wide eyes that stare up from below. Her outfit is the same one she wore for her outdoor performance

– and elicits the same excitement - but her hair is now gathered into a tight bun, sprigged with white myrtle and glittering feathers. In the half shadows, high up beneath the tent roof, she appears even smaller and more vulnerable, transformed into an ethereal vision by her spangles glinting in the light of the chandeliers. It is all too much for one member of the audience who calls out his undying love for her. Her quick reply, in a broad Lancashire accent, draws a ripple of surprised, nervous laughter from the visitors. This vision that hovers above them, as breakable as a china doll, is not only flesh and blood but appears to be one of their own.

With her balancing pole in her hands Zepha steps confidently onto the wire and hundreds of eyes follow her every move as she walks a distance of twenty feet to the other platform, pivots and returns to her starting point. She then repeats the walk but adds a small skip when she reaches the middle. The crowd gasp, their faces transfixed. On her third crossing she stops halfway, crouches down and leans slowly forward placing her balancing pole across the wire. As the crowd hold their breath, drums roll and she leans further over until her head is touching the wire and then, taking her weight on the pole, raises her legs into the air with careful deliberation. For a few agonising seconds the band falls silent, the audience is utterly still and it is only when her feet are once again safely in contact with the wire and the band strikes up that the crowd erupts, bawling and whistling.

To the delight of the Powell brothers the rest of her performance continues in much the same vein. A splicing of the graceful and mundane with the terrifying and incredulous. In one crossing of the wire she has her eyes covered with a blindfold and a sack placed over her head, relying entirely on supreme balance and the sensations in her feet. On another crossing her ankles are clamped with iron manacles linked by a long, heavy chain which clanks ominously with every small step. Then, a small wooden wheelbarrow is hoisted up to the platform and she pushes it steadily along the wire, its grooved front wheel the only device that keeps it from falling. Occasionally she appears to falter and the women and children in the audience clutch one another in fear (how can anyone, let alone a young woman, willingly put themselves in such a position of danger?) but their morbid curiosity prevents them from averting their eyes altogether and they watch, in rapt attention, as she completes her death-defying performance with one last dramatic stunt.

Returning to the platform Zepha places her feet into small wicker baskets of the sort more usually seen at market filled with peaches. The baskets are sealed around her calves and she gingerly manoeuvres out onto the wire with trembling, cautious footsteps, no longer able to feel it and relying purely on experience and strength of nerve to will her forward. It is a display of bravery, beauty and courage that, in the minds of the audience, defies all common sense and rational thinking and gives them gooseflesh.

On reaching the platform for the final time Zepha removes the baskets and turns to wave to the audience. Despite a lifetime of wire walking her hands are shaking and her heart is thumping like a hammer. The rush of adrenalin rises like a gorge in her throat. Every blood vessel in her head feels as though it's about to burst. Yet she is elated, her whole body filled with the sensation of conquering the world. A sensation she never tires of.

The ring master has a speech ready to whip up the enthusiasm of the audience but there really is no need. 'Madam Blondin' is everything her namesake could wish for. She has well and truly earned her money.

Addendum

The name Blondin was widely adopted by circus acts throughout the 1860s and '70s, even extending to wire-walking dogs and monkeys.

Zepha Davies continued to thrill the public with her highwire acts, travelling tirelessly around the country with her clown husband Robert and later adding two dogs to their act. By the end of the century they operated their own small circus company in Ireland and had five children who were all circus performers. Zepha died in 1912 at the age of seventy.

Sadly, not all female tight rope artistes were so fortunate. Many were exploited by unscrupulous managers with little regard to safety and in the early 1860s British newspapers reported a number of accidents, some fatal, which caused public outrage. By 1863, following the death of a tightrope performer who was heavily pregnant, calls were made for an Act of Parliament regulating such dangerous exhibitions and later that same year Queen Victoria wrote to the Mayor of Birmingham expressing her own strong views on the subject.

Chapter Seven

THE EQUESTRIANS

1870 Wednesday 13th July

Jenny Louise is tired, extraordinarily tired. Her elbow is tender from a recent fall and her right hamstring is tight and painful. Within her profession it is said that training to be a circus rider has only two possible outcomes - physical perfection or death, and at this moment she feels she's destined for the latter. Even the skin on her hip stings where it's been chafed by her new riding corset. Her old one virtually fell apart during their season in Bradford and she'll have to ask the wardrobe mistress to cut the new one higher to prevent it digging into her flesh. If, that is, she can find the time for such an errand.

Hengler's Grand Cirque opens for an eight-week run in Douglas tonight and Jenny Louise still has to ensure that her horses are familiar with the new setting before they're exposed to a demanding public. And how demanding they are! – content with nothing less than bright lights, variety, effortless performance and beaming smiles – smiles which Jenny Louise knows all too well hide a catalogue of long, exhausting days filled with tortuous repetition and often monotonous routine.

The company only arrived in the Isle of Man yesterday evening after a long taxing journey from Bradford and, like her, the horses are still recovering. But the entire company is under pressure. The name Hengler is a byword throughout the British Isles for exemplary circus entertainment and Jenny Louise's father Charles Hengler, the company's proprietor and director, is well known for his exacting standards. The company is still only halfway through the summer season and the Guv'nor, as he is known to those on his payroll, expects every man, woman and beast cavorting beneath his canvas roof to shine in the ring as though it is their first performance.

Fortunately for the animals, the Guv'nor took steps early on to ensure the stud's sea crossing to the Isle of Man was completed in relative comfort. A highly-trained circus horse is a valuable asset and several months ago Charles made an agreement with the Manx Steam Packet company to have their fast, new steamer 'Tynwald' fitted up with twenty loose boxes to ensure the stud's safe transportation. The 'Tynwald' has only been in service for the past four seasons and she is thankfully still in her prime - smart, comfortable and efficient, making the passage between Liverpool and Douglas in just four to five hours. With one groom assigned to every two horses, a plentiful supply of fresh water and hay, and some carefully administered equine sedatives, the animals all arrived in good condition.

Which is more than can be said for Jenny Louise. Her journey consisted of a few fitful hours sleep on a lumpy banquette, surrounded by the constant banter and tomfoolery of her circus cohorts. It is the height of the summer season and every available inch of the steamer's decks and cabins not occupied by passengers was crammed with Royal Mail deliveries, furniture and foodstuffs. It was only as Douglas harbour and the purple hills beyond came into view that Jenny Louise was able to push her way out onto the viewing deck in front of the wheelhouse and breathe in lungfuls of fresh sea air. There, she could almost feel like a performer again, against the exhilarating backdrop of thrashing paddle wheels, circling gulls and the deep vibrations of the ship's engines.

Despite the late hour as the steamer settled alongside the pier, the evening was still warm, scented with the tang of salt and seaweed. On the quay the last yellow rays of the sun bounced like tapers off shop windows, transforming dark, drab taverns into golden temples, streaking dirty glass with ribbons of fire. For a fleeting moment, Jenny Louise and her companions could almost be persuaded they had arrived in some exotic foreign resort - and a busy one at that. The very name Hengler is sufficient to promise entertainment in any guise and hundreds of summer visitors had rushed to the harbour straight after tea to watch the ship arrive, whirlpools of dark, oily water churning beneath her paddle boxes, thick black smoke belching from her funnels.

As the captain hurried to offload his passengers before the tide turned, the crowd pushed perilously close to the edge of the pier for a better view. A loud cheer went up as the circus band stepped onto the gangplank, banging their drums and blowing their trumpets, followed by the rest of the company, waving and pirouetting as they emerged into the evening sun, the town bathed in a warm pink glow. Once all the passengers had disembarked the horses were brought up from down below and led off down the gangplank under Charles Hengler's watchful eye. Dark, sleek, fine-boned stallions; patchwork ponies; broad-backed white horses spattered with dark grey splashes; and muscular, glossy black beasts with long frizzled manes and tails that swished the ground, stirring up a silvery haze of sand, coal dust and dried fish scales.

Charles had already been on the Island for a week to supervise the final stages of the construction of his new circus, and was pleased to be re-united with his daughter, who had little trouble spotting him in the crowd. He stands well over six feet tall and, although he's in his fiftieth year, still has the strong, upright physique of a man half his age, a stately bearing that can appear intimidating or persuasive, depending on his mood. His clothes are expensive and beautifully tailored. His well-trimmed hair, dark, thick and wavy, is parted with meticulous precision. His handsome face, half hidden by a luxuriant beard and moustache, is distinguished by an aquiline nose and hooded eyes that give him a somewhat inscrutable expression. To any bystander he has all the semblance of a refined gentleman, well-bred and orderly in his habits. It's only his extremely large, capable hands that hint he's as used to handling a skittish horse as handling a pen.

His daughter is out of a similar mould. She certainly shares his elongated, elegant bearing and hooded eyes, although in Jenny Louise, the latter simply make her appear shy and modest. She also has a smaller, dainty face with elfin chin which her legions of admirers describe as nothing less than beautiful. It's when sitting in a saddle though that she really becomes a Hengler, her slender frame shaped and sculpted by a formidable equestrian heritage and a lifetime spent adapting to the power and movement of a horse.

Which is exactly what has brought her to this point in her career. As she guides her bay mare Gazelle across the sawdust in rehearsal for opening night she steels herself against her tiredness. She is her father's second child and has ten siblings, the youngest of whom is only a baby, but while he's steered the younger ones towards a sound education he could not ignore Jenny Louise's potential as a rider. For the past five years, he has been training her and her horses and including her in his circus tours. Now, at the age of twenty one, she is already well travelled and has been taught by her father that mental and physical discipline will conquer even the most debilitating fatigue. Consequently, this afternoon she will take Gazelle through her 'leaping' act, practise with her fellow riders for the dance motions of the Quadrille, retire to her hotel for a short nap and a light tea, be seated, ready for her hairdresser by six o'clock, and mounted, ready to meet the public of the Isle of Man with her most gracious smile by nine o'clock prompt.

It has certainly raised Jenny Louise's spirits that, when compared to the industrial smoke and grime of Bradford, the new circus building built by her father in central Douglas seem little short of palatial.

Previously, visiting companies have set up in the green fields bordering the town's western perimeter but these have now been all but swallowed up in the race to build new streets and terraces. Charles therefore had to take a gamble on a setting that appears, at first glance, to be most unlikely. Towards the top of the rise overlooking the town there are two new streets – Hill and Myrtle – which form small arteries leading north away from St George's Church. Sandwiched between them is a large, walled timber yard owned by prominent local businessman Henry Noble, consisting of little more than a wide-open space with a few small workshops pinned around its edges. The yard had been lying unused for a while and Noble was more than happy to rent it to Charles for two months for the sum of forty-two pounds - plus a little negotiation on a ready supply of sawdust.

It was the location, however, that really appealed to Charles, this part of the metropolis having become the hub of summer visitor accommodation in recent years. Sufficiently raised above the smoke-filled, malodorous town, numerous fashionable lodging houses now fan out in all directions along the top of the hill, with banks, shops, livery stables and the post office nearby, and all within easy walking distance of the timber yard.

And in a most opportune twist of fate it would appear that Hengler's Cirque will also have its own divine protection, for the timber yard is placed slap bang between two houses of God – St George's Anglican Church a few yards to the south and the new Roman Catholic church of St Mary's on the north. If Hengler's do not experience good fortune on this island there will surely be questions at Sunday prayers!

Only a matter of weeks after signing the lease agreement a local firm of building contractors began work within the walls of the timber yard and soon completed the erection of a substantial wooden cirque covered with a sturdy canvas roof. From the outside it is not the most attractive of buildings, resembling little more than a giant wooden casket, plain and featureless, with no windows and only slatted vents for the free flow of air within. At one end is an entrance for gentle-folk, giving them access to the pit, boxes, amphitheatre and stalls. At the other end, simple folk who have only sixpence in their pocket can be admitted to the gallery.

But this is a building that can seat sixteen hundred people at any one time and any money spared on the exterior has been lavished on the interior, a spacious and colourful hippodrome incorporating the standard forty-two foot ring, circled by a variety of seating arrangements. A wide promenade runs around the whole building enabling the audience to move freely from one area to another, there's a splendid lounge for pre-show refreshments and behind the auditorium there are roomy stables to house the entire stud, as well as the usual wardrobes and dressing saloons for the performers.

Admission prices range up to three shillings, considerably more than the Manx public are used to paying, but then, the facilities and high standards offered by this circus are more than they are used to getting. Great attention has been given to comfort, especially in the stalls where the upholsterers have been busy. Cane chairs are lined with cushioned padding and the floor is covered with a richly coloured carpet; in the amphitheatre the narrow wooden benches with hard upright backs are softened by the addition of plush crimson velvet. Even in the raised benches of the sixpenny gallery Charles Hengler insists on providing space, good ventilation and a clear view of the ring if nothing else. Although by sheer luck the gallery is located directly above Mr Clement's first class band, giving music lovers in the cheap seats an unexpected bonus. Plus, they have the best view of the gangway which connects the ring with the stables.

The whole construction may only be temporary but Hengler's Cirque is a monument to detail. Even now, in the height of summer, a plentiful supply of fresh air will ensure the audience is kept cool and unpleasant smells are kept to a minimum. Natural light is sparse but that is more than made up for by the numerous wall-mounted gas jets and glittering chandeliers which hang from chains at various points around the building. In fact, during a performance, the white light is so bright it almost hurts the eyes. The ceiling is covered with coloured folds of chintz and the pillars supporting the roof are neatly papered and ornamented with flags and shields.

It is the performers and their superb steeds, however, that the public of the Isle of Man are really coming to see and tonight, beneath this vibrant canopy, they will have a rare chance to see what Charles Hengler promises will be a virtuoso display of horsemanship. Farmers and farriers from all over the Island are expected to attend, alongside horse racing enthusiasts, cab drivers, genteel young ladies, military men and livery boys, as well as the usual multitude of holidaymakers and their excitable children. Charles is determined they will be dazzled by a visual feast of superlative riding, from the raw skill of bareback to the formality of haute école.

Anyone hoping for bare flesh and sensationalism is likely to be disappointed. Recent years have seen a rise in riders who flaunt themselves, and acts that rely on danger and vulgarity, but there's nothing of that here. The Guv'nor simply will not tolerate it. During the years in which he's been perfecting his equestrian shows in Britain's major cities he has gained a name for respectability and propriety, reminiscent, some say, of Astley's in its heyday. His horses are highly trained and pampered. His riders are experienced and intelligent. Everything about his establishments is punctilious and inoffensive. An evening at Hengler's is a guarantee of rational entertainment for the whole family, carried off with the precision of a piece of clockwork. In his company the men are men, and the women are women. Shams, charlatans and salacious behaviour have no place in a Hengler concern.

Jenny Louise mulls this over as she prepares for her opening debut in front of a Manx audience. Her father's emphasis on decency and taste is especially evident in the wardrobe department and to this end she will appear tonight in the dark, sober habit of a lady riding to hounds. She rides side-saddle, naturally, and her outfit, although plain and decidedly unspectacular, requires time and effort to assemble. It's fortunate that she's not due to appear until the evening programme is halfway through. First her dresser helps her into her newly-adjusted riding corset, an expensive item, made to order and fashioned in such a way that the stays lie higher than normal to allow her to adopt a comfortable sitting position. When the laces are pulled tight it also protects her torso from too much damage should she fall off her horse or be kicked in the ribs. Over her corset she wears a fine cotton shirt with a lace collar, and around her neck she winds a long cream silk stock, finished with a bow. It is stiff and restrictive but will also help protect her neck and spine if she becomes unseated. Over the shirt she wears a tight-fitting wool jacket, fastened to the neck with a dozen buttons, the generously cut gigot-style sleeves allowing her plenty of movement at the elbow.

Her lower half is all about dressing to accommodate the peculiarities of riding side saddle. When seated she will face her horse's head with her right leg bent and her left leg straight. Her hard-wearing drawers are made of the softest chamois leather, her petticoat is white cotton lawn and her plain, dark wool skirt is fitted at the waist, flaring out in full, generous gathers. It is unusually long, draping a good six inches below her feet to ensure her limbs are entirely covered from view when in the saddle, and when she walks from her dressing room to the stables, she drapes the bulk of the fabric around her right hip and fastens it at the centre back with a button and ribbon loop to avoid dragging it in the dirt.

Her formal ensemble is finished with a black silk top hat, firmly pinned onto her long, lustrous dark hair which her hairdresser has worked on for over an hour, braiding and coiling it into an elaborate pile on the back of her head. Unlike her fellow equestriennes she wears little in the way of paste or paint on her face, merely opting for a small dab of crème celeste to disguise the dark shadows beneath her eyes, a light dusting of pearl powder and some beeswax to soothe her cracked lips. Only the addition of delicate, drop earrings and a wide taffeta sash around the crown of her hat soften her otherwise stern and sober appearance.

As Jenny Louise finishes the last details to her costume on this opening night, over a thousand people have gathered outside the cirque waiting for the show to start. Local traders vie for their custom, drawing them to wooden trays piled high with currant pastries, meat pies, toffee, gingerbread, comfits, lemonade and jough, the local ale. The traders would prefer to ply their wares within the aisles of the cirque but Charles Hengler will hear none of it and won't allow them on his premises. Likewise, anyone who wishes to enjoy a cigar or a pipe will have to do so before they enter his hallowed walls as smoking is strictly forbidden. The Guv'nor has seen too many circus buildings go up in flames. It is said he won't even allow his company members to smoke pipes in the street and frowns upon the chewing of tobacco. Though that is more to prevent the grooms spitting their filth on the floor of the stables.

Within twenty minutes of the doors being opened to the public those very grooms are being marshalled by the circus manager, William Powell. Every seat, he informs them, has been taken. The cirque is fairly bursting at the seams. By this stage of the evening every performing horse should have been brushed until it gleams, its hooves scrubbed and oiled, all tack polished and buffed, and buckles and straps checked and double checked. The horses feel the urgency in his voice and stamp their feet in their stalls, jerking against their ropes and pricking their ears as the head stud groom walks down the line for a last-minute inspection. They know his step and whinny as he comes near, snuffling his pockets for apples or lumps of sugar. The new stables have only been occupied for a couple of days but already they carry the strong, sweet, fermented smell of hay which spills from the racks that extend along the back wall. Long working days make for hungry horses and the forage supplier from town has done a good job, providing them with a small mountain of hay and chaff, bins full of oats and barley and sacks brimming with turnips and carrots.

The stables are warm and steamy with the heat from the animals and already cluttered with all the accoutrements of a busy workshop. Grooming gear and harnesses hang from wooden pegs fixed around the walls, paraffin lamps hang from ceiling hooks and everywhere there are brooms, water pails and brushes. The day began early.

At five o'clock the horses were taken down to Douglas beach for an invigorating gallop along the sands while stable lads mucked out the stalls and laid down clean straw. Then it was time for washing and feeding before the local farrier arrived to trim the horse's hooves and check their legs. At ten the performers arrived to take them through their paces in the ring – leaping over bars and gates, jumping through hoops and drums, picking up handkerchiefs, dancing, bowing, truly everything that could be asked of a quadruped to satisfy a curious public.

On entering the ring the performers had passed William Powell accompanied by a young man on a fine young horse. Never one to waste an opportunity Charles Hengler has arranged for William to offer daily riding lessons to the paying gentry of both sexes and it's no surprise to the Guv'nor that the sessions are already well subscribed. William's riding abilities are second only to his legendary good looks and charisma.

By the time the Director of the Circle, Mr Felix Revolti, enters the ring fence to begin the evening's performance the atmosphere in the audience is at fever pitch, the air in the cirque is thick and humid despite the numerous air vents and there is a cloying smell of sticky sugar, warm pastry and horse dung. With a flourish from the band and a familiar crack of the whip the greatly anticipated entertainment opens with a young man named Moffatt entering the ring on the back of a cantering horse. His horse is heavier than a typical nag on the street, but good looking, fit and strong, with striking markings in brown and white. Its head is bowed, its neck arched and held firm by a restraining strap that is fixed to its saddle pad.

As Mr Revolti settles the horse to a steady pace, anti-clockwise around the edges of the ring, its young rider jumps to a standing position, his feet placed hip width apart on the horse's wide back. The audience are instantly filled with admiration. How is such a feat possible without the rider losing his balance? Their eyes tell them the horse is certainly sure-footed enough but what they cannot see is the mathematics behind the spectacle. For it is the precise measurement of the ring – Philip Astley's magical forty-two foot diameter – that is helping the horse achieve the perfect pace and speed, and maintain it in a regular rhythm. More importantly, it gives Mr Moffat the perfect centrifugal force to maintain his balance. As the horse circles the ring both horse and rider are leaning inwards, and as Mr Moffatt proceeds to leap over banners and through hoops from the back of his steed, he lands at exactly the same angle, accommodating his centre of gravity to that of his horse.

Mr Moffatt's experience also belies his youthful appearance. Apprenticed at the age of seven, he was then young, small and light enough for his broken bones and bruises to heal quickly after he tumbled. Had his training begun any later it would have been much more difficult.

For the next half hour the varieties come thick and fast and they are all most pleasant and entertaining. There's Mr Powell and his pretty little pony Merrylegs, which he encourages to dance and bow for the delighted audience. He's too tall to ride the pony so employs the help of a long whip and a pocketful of treats to conduct her from the sawdust. Then there is Mademoiselle Rebecca Rochez, a dainty young teen and leading artiste with Hengler's for the past five years, who proceeds to jump through a succession of hoops on horseback. The only shadow over her performance is the whisper that her widowed mother is an invalid and entirely supported by her only child. Many of the ladies in the audience vow to leave a few extra pennies for brave Miss Rochez when they leave the cirque.

By the time Mr Revolti announces Charles Fillis and his young son's gymnastic feats on horseback the audience are nicely warmed up and ready for some real thrills. Mr Fillis is known throughout England and the Continent as 'the great somersault and pirouette artiste' and the young farmers jostling for position in the gallery are intrigued. They can hardly imagine such a scenario.

To a thundering drum roll, a slight young man and a young boy canter into the ring mounted on two eye-catching horses. Mr Fillis senior is riding a tall, solidly built, Danish Knabstrupper, its distinctive white coat densely splattered with dark grey smears, trailing a gloriously thick white mane and tail. It is a powerful horse with the baroque conformation that makes it so well suited to this kind of work - broad, heavily muscled hindquarters, good legs and a thick, muscular, arched neck. The boy is riding a smaller horse, pure white, but also broad in the frame, with heavy, rippling muscles and a fat rump. Both animals appear keen and eager, apparently immune to the barrage of loud music and thousand voices that fill the auditorium.

The first half of the act consists of father and son riding behind and alongside one another, switching positions at speed from horse's back to the ground and back again, flipping, twirling and even lying across their horses' withers. The father is small, light and as agile as a cat. The boy is as bouncy and bendy as Indian rubber. At one point, Mr Fillis even moves his son up on to his shoulders as he hurtles around the ring. The children in the pit are wide-eyed and clamp their hands across their mouths to stop from crying out, while others, afraid to watch, peek nervously between their fingers. Fortunately, their fears are unfounded and the boy leaves the circle unscathed, leaving his father to rise to a standing position on his horse's back. The audience lean forward as one body, anticipating something novel and thrilling.

While the horse is moving Mr Fillis positions his feet close to the base of the horse's mane and, as it passes the orchestra, launches himself in a neat backwards somersault, landing on his feet on the horse's wide rump. He then swiftly returns to his starting position and performs a half backwards somersault, landing on his hands and completing the movement by springing from his hands to the floor.

All is going well until, suddenly, a brown paper bag unexpectedly floats down from the gallery. The panicked horse shies and stumbles and Mr Fillis, caught in mid-flight, appears destined for a nasty fall. But then, with the most extraordinary quick thinking, he catches the horse's back with his foot as he falls and spins into the sawdust, rolled up in a protective ball. As Mr Revolti quietens the horse and urges it back into its circular rhythm Mr Fillis rises, waving and smiling to the audience, leaps nimbly onto the horse's moving back, and successfully repeats the somersault as calmly as a man playing bowls.

Having gained the full, mesmerised attention of the crowd, Mr Fillis suddenly changes tack, slowing his horse to a trot and flopping onto the thick pad on its back. The horse's ears twitch as he talks to it and together they move into the centre of the circle. Mr Revolti announces that Mr Fillis will now display the complex training manoeuvre known as the pirouette, and this time it's the turn of the military men in the side boxes to sit up and take notice. Any cavalry officer worth his salt knows that for a man to be able to fight hand-to-hand on horseback his horse must have the strength and ability to turn on the spot, at speed and with great agility. The pirouette is one of the most demanding aspects of military training and not always attainable. This will be well worth watching.

For what seems like an age, Mr Fillis stands his horse perfectly still until the band commences a slow marching song. As the music gathers pace the horse begins to move its shoulders and front legs in a circle, pivoting on its hindquarters while keeping its hind feet in the centre of the circle. Mr Fillis appears to be hardly moving, only the merest pressure of his legs persuading the horse to bend its body in the direction of the movement. The music grows faster. The horse moves faster. Soon the march is in full swing and both horse and rider are pirouetting like a dancer in the corps de ballet. And then, just as suddenly, the horse slows to a halt and begins to move in the opposite direction, faster, faster, round and round, its head bobbing, its hind legs creating a whirlwind of tanbark and sawdust. In their boxes, the military men thump the floor with their boots in recognition of a kindred spirit.

With the conclusion of Mr Fillis's turn, there is a seamless transition to the next, and the next, and the next, the audience swept along in an exhausting parade of fearless and illuminating equestrian exhibitions. Young men shout themselves hoarse, boys wave their caps and ladies' maids enjoying an evening off clap their red hands until they're raw.

In the performers' waiting area, Jenny Louise Hengler stands with her mare Gazelle, preparing to enter the ring. Her earlier fatigue has become a vague numbness and her only concern now is the welfare of her horse. Gazelle has been brought up from the stables and stands ready in the waiting area behind the gallery. By any standards she is a splendid animal. The grooms have done a masterful job, strapping and brushing her coat, mane and tail to a deep shine; her conformation is good with straight, clean legs and a well-balanced stance, and the deep muscles of her sloping shoulders twitch in anticipation. From beneath her forelock she watches the activity backstage with large, liquid brown eyes that are bright and full of expression, and her ears indicate that she's constantly listening to her surroundings – pricking forward each time the crowd roars, before flicking around to the voice of the groom as he checks the side saddle and breastplate and tightens her girths.

And while her mistress's habit is plain and utilitarian Gazelle's equipments can only be described as beautiful, fashioned with great care by the calloused, patient hands of a saddler entrusted by the Henglers for many years. The dipped seat and side flaps of the side saddle are made of burnished, tan-coloured pigskin, minutely stitched and decoratively finished with a unique, hand-tooled pattern. Two raised pommels at the front of the saddle protrude from the leather like blunt horns and the linen lining is deeply padded with sheep's wool, shaped to create a wide gullet over Gazelle's backbone. Every inch has been made to measure. No other horse will wear this saddle and no other rider will sit upon it.

At a signal from William Powell, Jenny Louise steps forward to mount her horse, clutching all four reins and a silver-topped cane in her left hand and gripping the rear end of the saddle with the other, the bulk of her skirt draped over her left arm. A stable hand holds the mare's head as another man stands alongside her and forms his hands into a cradle. The second man is not a groom but dressed for the ring in frock coat, riding boots and breeches and he and Jenny Louise exchange a few quiet words as she places her left foot into his hands and is bounced up to sit sideways on the saddle. The man pats the mare's neck and talks to her in Polish, making Jenny Louise laugh. Herr Oscar has been employed by her father for his way with horses, but it's no secret within the company that he also appears to have a certain way with Charles Hengler's daughter.

After adjusting her skirt Jenny Louise turns so that she is facing Gazelle's ears and discreetly moves her limbs into position. To the public in the auditorium it will appear as though she is sitting comfortably in an easy chair, but they are unaware of the two pommels designed to keep her firm in her seat. With her modesty protected by her habit, she raises her right knee and hooks it over-and-under the high pommel which curves to the right. Her thigh is now firmly braced, extending forward, and her knee bends sideways across Gazelle's withers, allowing her lower leg to rest against the horse's left shoulder. Her other leg is blessedly allowed a more natural position, hanging down with her foot in a stirrup.

All that is needed now is the smallest of movements, an imperceptible shift of her weight to the right so that her left side is raised ever so slightly off the saddle. In her early days this would cause her muscles to ache dreadfully but hundreds of hours on horseback have educated them well. Once she's adjusted her position to her own satisfaction Jenny Louise is sitting completely straight, as though an invisible thread runs through her back and her horse's tail. With all contrivances and apparatus hidden from view she is a picture of elegance, grace and femininity.

They enter the bright lights of the cirque to a roar of approval. Gazelle is startled for only a second or two, before relaxing into the routine she knows so well. The band is in full swing and the audience moves and sways like turbulent water. Jenny Louise holds her head high, smiling and nodding to the crowd, erect and virtually motionless in the saddle, moving in perfect harmony with her mount as she urges Gazelle to a canter.

For the next fifteen minutes she holds the audience spellbound as she takes Gazelle over a series of banners, bars and hurdles that become increasingly higher and more difficult. With each jump she feels a dig in her left thigh as her leg is gripped by the 'leaping head' pommel that prevents her from losing her seat. By the last round she is flying over a five-barred gate and the crowd go wild, cheering and waving at this bold, petite young woman and her wonderful steed.

On leaving the ring Jenny Louise quickly gathers her habit and twists out of her saddle. Herr Oscar is waiting to catch her as she slips to the ground. Her limbs are tingling with adrenalin but her head is thumping and she feels hot and clammy inside her tight jacket, her shirt soaked with sweat. She's due to appear in the ring again towards the end of the night and will use the next half hour to rub balsam into her joints and bathe her feet in cool water.

As she leaves the ring another man is preparing to enter it. At thirty-seven years old Anthony Bridges no longer has youth on his side, but more than makes up for it in terms of experience and sheer fearlessness. By the age of ten he was already a seasoned performer in his father's circus, tagged as 'The Equestrian Phenomenon', and his older brother Selim, who spent a season in the Isle of Man with Mr Batty, taught him everything he knows. For almost thirty years Anthony has earned a good living performing such feats as his famous jockey act, in which he dispenses with saddle and bridle and hurtles around the ring with arms folded, at an angle of forty-five degrees, while the whole company assail him with a fusillade of shouts and whip-cracks. In tonight's performance he's partnered with his best Friesian horse, a resolutely cheerful and willing companion. This, some say, is the breed that carried German knights to the Crusades. Unfazed and unruffled under even the most trying circumstances, he's a small, compact animal, coal black with a dramatically long mane and tail and feathered legs, a curiously boxy physique with powerful shoulders and short, strong legs. But more importantly for Mr Bridges, it is plain that this particular horse has absolute trust in its master, gained, he tells his own sons, from years of close handling and sacks full of carrots.

The horse was four years old before it was considered ready for training and, even then, it took a year to get it to the stage it is now. A simple shaft of sunlight, a shadow or a pocket handkerchief caught on the breeze can spook even the calmest animal and many hours were spent acclimatizing it to the noise, lights and chaos of a packed hippodrome. Painstakingly, over a period of many weeks, the horse had paper-covered hoops broken over its head, a whip cracked close to its body, programmes waved in its face and teams of grooms and stable hands shouting on all sides. It took time and great patience but the horse is brave and loyal and it gradually increased in confidence until it attained the complete nonchalance it is showing tonight.

With the jockeying accomplished, and the Friesian duly rewarded, it is then the turn of a sturdy piebald stallion to take to the circle.

As it establishes a steady canter, Mr Bridges adopts a sideways standing position on the horse's back with his legs apart and his back to the audience. A clown throws him three oranges and for the next two circuits of the ring he proceeds to juggle the fruit as easily as if he was standing on a stage. He then discards the oranges and in quick succession repeats the process with three tin plates, three wooden clubs and, to the crowd's incredulity, three large knives, before concluding by circling the ring at speed spinning a plate on the top of a long thin pole. It's a stunning display, that leaves the audience exhausted. And not all can handle it. The volatile combination of adrenalin and heat beneath the canvas roof has caused a number of ladies to faint and an entire row of hysterical small children has had to be removed to the fresh air. It's with some relief that Mr Revolti announces the final act on the programme and a complete change of pace.

As the audience take a few minutes to purchase refreshments from the lounge, Charles Hengler and seven of his star performers assemble in the horse corridor in preparation for the Lancers' Quadrille - a virtuoso display of high school riding set to music and performed like a dance. Charles, alongside Herr Oscar, Anthony Bridges and William Powell, dressed in full military uniform, will accompany Jenny Louise and three other lady riders in a spectacle that demonstrates a level of skill and training rarely seen in day-to-day life, summing up, in a way, everything that Charles Hengler holds dear – discipline, elegance, decency and good order.

The Quadrille is led by Jenny Louise, perfectly poised on her high school horse Shamrock, a stunning 16-hands half thoroughbred, caparisoned with saddle cloth pad, side saddle and gilded bridle and she leads her fellow riders into the ring to a lively military-style waltz. The ladies are identically attired in plain but elegant hunting habits and top hats, the men wear matching cream jodhpurs, red military jackets with gold epaulettes, peaked, plumed helmets, white gloves and gold sashes across the chest. Even the horses are perfectly suited, each pairing identical in colour, size and length of stride. The audience murmur their approval, whispers of 'enchanting' and 'gorgeous' echoing around the auditorium.

To begin, the horses walk behind one another in a perfect line before breaking into a slow, measured trot and, with only the merest pressure of a leg or touch of a rein, sweep into a figure of eight. They then break off in alternate directions, assembling four on each side before trotting diagonally across each other in a demonstration of exquisite precision, a flowing, seamless ribbon of movement. With the merest turn of her head Jenny Louise then gathers her band of followers to form a square in the centre of the ring, a male and female rider on each side, facing inwards. The men salute and the women bow their heads as Mr Clement urges the band to change tempo and the riders proceed to dance towards, across and around each other in a controlled, gentle canter. The music is perfectly matched to the pace of the horses and so familiar to them that each bar prompts the required movement with hardly any guidance from their riders. As they brush stirrups the couples could be forgiven for indulging in small talk and whispered endearments as they draw near and around each other before slipping away. As it is, every time Jenny Louise passes Herr Oscar their heads almost touch and a keen observer might even glimpse the young woman blush.

It is a dance of pure symmetry. A dreamlike sequence, throughout which the audience remain curiously stilled, holding their breath. Everything is perfectly controlled, deliberate, unhurried. Only at the conclusion of the dance are the horses allowed to show their pleasure, lining up in a perfectly straight row, snorting and nodding their heads and pawing the ground. At the head of the line Shamrock bows to the audience, drooping his neck, extending one leg and lowering his other knee to the ground as his mistress pats his neck and waves to the crowd, still erect, still smiling and mercifully still in one piece. The crowd, in turn, allow themselves to breathe once more and roar in appreciation, clamouring for more. But it's not to be. Out on the street carriages and dumb nags are waiting. Jenny Louise has placed an order with her hotel for a late supper of beef tea and sandwiches. The company have an eight-week season to fulfil and their work has only just begun.

Addendum

Later the same year Charles Fillis took his act to the New York Circus, while Rebecca Rochez married Mr Moffatt and headed for Portugal.

In 1872 a young man died after the gallery of Hengler's Circus in Sheffield collapsed, throwing eighty people to the ground. Evidence showed that heavy rain had caused the side of the building to 'buckle' and it was noted that in future such buildings should be examined by a surveyor before they were opened to the public.

In 1874 Jenny Louise Hengler married her equestrian partner Count Waldemar Alexander Oscar Kamienski on May 6th at Marylebone parish church in London. The couple, who went by the name Mr and Mrs Oscar, headed to America in 1877 for a six-month engagement with Barnum's Circus.

Anthony Bridges, the scenic act rider and juggler, died in January 1879 aged just forty-six. Later that month Hengler's Circus advertised his two sons, aged eleven and fourteen, as prospective equestrian apprentices.

Charles Hengler died suddenly in the autumn of 1887 at his Hampstead residence, having spent the previous week at his estate in Gloucestershire. He was known to suffer bronchitis and had in previous years wintered on the Devon coast. For many years he ran permanent circuses in Edinburgh, Glasgow, Liverpool, Hull, Dublin and London and was survived by his three sons Walter, Frederick and Albert and six daughters. His estate was valued at just under sixty thousand pounds.

Chapter Eight

THE JESTER, THE HARLEQUIN & THE CLOWN

1871 Friday 25th August

"Sharp weather, Splasher!"

"Yes, indeed, sir."

"Capital weather for the race, eh?"

"The race? What race is that sir?"

"Why Splasher, the human race of course!"

The silver-haired gentleman in the corner of the salon is looking through the pages of a large leather-bound notebook and chortles to himself when he comes across this jest, written in his own handwriting only a few weeks ago. For through the rain-lashed window behind him there is such a foul tempest that it's hard to believe it's only late August. He's been in Douglas for just over a week and for the past five days the weather has been anything but capital.

Wild storms screaming across the Irish Sea have certainly tested the resolve – and stomachs – of those visitors enticed here by the promise of rest and recreation. Two thousand have arrived since Monday alone and the majority, once dumped on the quayside, look rather as if they have been to hell and back, their factory faces pale and wan, their clothes damp and crumpled. It's hardly the stuff of precious holidays but for the silver-haired gentleman it provides an unexpected bonus, for his services are likely to be appreciated more than ever.

'The renowned Queen's Jester' William Frederick Wallett – Bill to his friends - is here for a short engagement with the Great United Circus of Hayes, Harvey & Hayes, who have pulled together a small travelling company of clowns, acrobats and equestrians for a tenting stint on Britain's golden holiday island. Not that it currently feels 'golden' and oh, what a time to be in a tent! Yesterday evening the storm appeared to reach its zenith, shattering roof tiles, pulling up trees by their roots and flinging litter round the streets and harbour like a whirling dervish. The saving grace for William Hayes and Dan Harvey is that they've been able to erect their tent within the walls of the still-vacant timber yard where Hengler's were last year, offering them some welcome shelter.

And fortunately for Bill Wallett, he and his wife, alongwith their two young children, a maid servant and man servant, are staying in a house just fifty yards from the circus site. Tonight, he will only have to make a short walk to fulfil his engagement and can be back in the safety of his comfortable lodgings with his darling family and a large brandy by the time the cirque has emptied.

But for now, he has work to do. At lunch he dined on turbot, devilled kidneys and fruit trifle at the Imperial Hotel on the Quay and has since settled himself in the hotel salon with his notebook and a glass of port, ready to amuse anyone who has the time to listen to his stories of life as the self-proclaimed 'Queen's Jester'. And he's attracted quite a crowd. For hours he has fixated hotel guests with tales told in his rich Yorkshire baritone of personal adventures on both sides of the Atlantic – from the mountains of Mexico to the vibrant streets of Paris. His notebook is on his knee and as he talks he occasionally glances at it, plucking out references that fly through the air like the debris in the streets outside – intriguing phrases such as 'gold nuggets', 'Christy Minstrels' and 'silver salver'. Every now and then he pauses and takes a slow, measured sip of his port, allowing a large diamond ring on his hand to glint in the gas light.

Even regardless of his mellifluous voice Bill Wallett cuts a charismatic figure. Strongly built and radiating energy, he has sharp, piercing eyes; mobile, expressive facial features and a high receding hairline that gives way to a thick head of hair. Puffy bags beneath his eyes and silver-grey streaks in his full moustache and narrow goatee beard underscore his sixty-plus years, but, as he warms to his topics and prompts his small audience to laughter, his whole face lights up and his eyes dance with the merriment of a mischievous juvenile.

"If I rest, I rust" is a phrase oft used in the Wallett household and, true to form, on arrival in the Isle of Man his carpet bag was stuffed full of the advertising literature that is always kept well stocked in the basement of his home. His advance posters have already alerted the population that 'Wallett is Coming!' Now, he has day bills distributed all over town stating simply that 'Wallett is Here!' His name is top of the show's bill, as per his contract, and he has supplied the local newspapers with two entire columns of glowing, recent press reviews and details of his many gifts and presentations from admirers and benefactors (with an additional word on the quiet that this could well be his last tour before retirement and the public are advised to see him before he disappears into the annals of entertainment history).

The name Wallett is known, of course, throughout the land. It's nearly thirty years since he appeared before Her Majesty and the Royal Family at Windsor and ever since then he has been fêted by all levels of society, entertaining entire generations from elderly matrons to babes in arms with his satirical jests, comic philosophy and classical speeches. Tonight is his Benefit Night and if it attracts the bumper audiences predicted by the management then he should find his earnings substantially boosted by a large share of the takings. Hence, this inclement afternoon spent in the lounge of a smart hotel promises to be time well spent. By this evening he will have tickled the underbelly of the Isle of Man and left it hungry for more.

Later, in the cramped, canvas-sided dressing room of Hayes, Harvey & Hayes Circus on Hill Street, 'The Great W.F.Wallett' is still not done with his publicity drive. He is a keen advocate of the new photography techniques and has had fifty daguerreotype portraits made to be given out to the first fifty patrons to enter the cirque. And he is equally generous with his wisdom. He's recently had his autobiography published and tonight the other merrymen who share the dressing room will all enjoy the benefit of his experience. The youngest, Nat Emmett, has been performing since he could walk but Wallett still taunts him that he was drawing crowds in New York when Emmett was only the height of a milking stool.

The clown's dressing room is a curious place, a humid, smoky cavern reminiscent of a Bohemian artist's studio. The air is heavy with the pungent scent of male sweat, mingled with the rich, acrid odours of molten tallow, pomade, pigment powders and used-clothing. Every available inch is crammed with bodies, furniture and strange garments. Wooden-framed looking glasses perch precariously on dressing tables piled high with a jumble of tin cups, miniature saucepans and making-up boxes containing hares' feet, brushes, powders, matches, candles and spirit gum. Stained rags fight for space alongside damp towels draped across bentwood chairs. Boxes jammed in every corner spill over with wigs, spangled fabrics and mysterious props, and colourful hats and costumes hang on all sides from makeshift pegs.

The conversation within the room is equally as diverse and fascinating. Even as the giant canvas marquee shudders and strains noisily in the wind, Wallett can be heard reminding his cohorts that although a true clown is born, not made, he must still constantly read, listen and look at the ordinary in order to find the extra-ordinary. As an example, he quotes the season of 1862 when a gentleman was seen returning to the International Exhibition every day to look closely at the workings of Mr Benson's large clock. Was he an horologist come to admire a fine piece of engineering? A lover of mechanics? A rival clockmaker seeking to make a secret copy of this wondrous machine? No, he was simply a clown looking for new sources of comic inspiration where others could only see a maze of wheels and levers.

With the timing of a seasoned professional Wallett's last words are uttered just as Nat Emmett is called to the ring with his performing goat Esmerelda. He's worked with animals since he was a boy, namely his parents' Newfoundland dogs and a rescued dancing bear, but the goat is his favourite.

Singing a comic song and carrying a chair he leads the goat into the centre of the ring where both trainer and quadruped greet the audience with a low bow. Dressed in outlandish white frills and long pumps, his face painted white and slashed with red and black, Nat persuades the goat to demonstrate its docility by walking on its knees, standing on its hind legs, marching to the strains of the band and jumping over a half a dozen chairs. As he does so Nat imitates the goat with overblown movements and gestures that cause the audience to howl with laughter. Occasionally gusts of wind ram the canvas sides of the tent causing the goat to shy and bleat but her trainer adeptly weaves these little nuances into the show and they leave the circle to enthusiastic applause.

The next few minutes pass in a flurry of activity. A handful of young boys enter the circle with buckets to clean up after the goat and the sawdust is raked as two lithe figures brightly costumed in spangled diamonds, spots and stripes run around the ring fence diverting small children with woollen cod-fish. But then the ring curtain billows and a grey, bearded head pops out, the bells on his dark, three-pointed cap jingling.

"Welcome you! How now, you! What, you! Fellow, you! And thus much for greeting. Now, my spruce companions, is all ready and all things neat?" The audience roars with approval. Wallett, the great Wallett, Shakespearean fool and jester to their beloved Queen Victoria, is amongst them. The curtains are fully parted and Wallett strolls solemnly into the ring, bauble in hand, bowing in a circle to all levels of the audience. As a jester, he has no need for face paint and conveys his character simply through his imposing physical presence and striking, elegant motley of long-sleeved blue silk tunic, trimmed at the collar and cuffs with the narrowest of white ruffs and finely embroidered with three Royal lions and other patriotic emblems. His blue satin knee length breeches are likewise embroidered with faces, feathers and baubles and below the knee he wears plain white tights and soft white kid elastic-sided boots embellished with red silk rosettes.

The crowd grows silent as Wallett begins to speak, their ears straining to catch his every syllable above the howling wind. But they needn't worry. His voice is remarkable - deep, resonant and powerful, every word beautifully enunciated, every consonant clipped, every vowel elongated. His Yorkshire brogue is hardly noticeable as he launches into his own version of the Fool's speech from King Lear.

It is a word-perfect delivery, rich with comic inflections and the audience, whether simple or educated, lap up every syllable. For the great Wallett is actually addressing them. He is speaking directly to them. And they love it.

Even the smallest children - of which there are many – enjoy the chance to simply laugh for the sake of laughing at this strangely-dressed man.

Moreover, it's clear to the Douglas audience that this clown is anything but a fool. For the next fifteen minutes 'The Queen's Jester' plays with their emotions like a fiddler with his bow, tossing words into the air and bouncing them like a juggler's clubs, flinging them into the gallery and watching them ripple and reverberate. Sometimes they fall flat, dulled by the ignorance of the recipients, but more often they fly and soar; droll notes, acerbic notes, stinging sarcasms, dazzling witticisms, each syllable a perfectly-pitched note, each phrase a cadence. Pithy observations pour from his lips, sharp arrows find their targets. Not a pun is wasted, every quip is insightful, carefully constructed and delivered with weight and eloquence. "Never confide in a young man – new pails leak". "Never tell your secret to the aged – old doors seldom shut closely!"

His vocabulary has a life and rhythm that sweeps his audience along with him. He plucks, he slides, he pulls up sharply, changes pace, babbles and mutters, before slowly building into a thundering oratory, words spitting and spraying as a thousand faces form silent 'Oh!'s.

The crowd are unsure whether to laugh or cry. This jester's ability to show up the vices and follies of the age and hold a mirror to their own weaknesses is at times uncomfortable - and yet he's done it with such wit that they have split their sides! The man is truly a marvel.

It is as physical and draining a performance as any regular buffoon's and when Wallett finally leaves the circle to make room for the equestrians he retreats to the dressing room where he removes his cap and calls his manservant to bring his jest book so that he can rehearse his next lines. The dog-eared book holds a lifelong collection of jokes, observations, speeches, quotations, poems, songs and ditties, and next to his family it is his most precious possession. He will have three more entrées, or set pieces, tonight and although he still has an extraordinary memory the book is a wonderful buffer against the onset of decrepitude.

As Wallett settles to his lines a small, muscular man sits down alongside him at a cluttered dressing table. The man is dressed in the frills of a clown but has a towel over his collar, his nuggety face is naked and freshly shaved and his hair is little more than thin stubble. He takes another towel from the chair and rubs his whole head vigorously until it is completely dry then, from a well-travelled making-up box, he takes a thick, mutton tallow candle and rubs it briskly between his warm hands until the tallow melts into an oily unguent. Using both hands he smears the pungent grease over his head, face and neck, working it into the fine creases of his skin and ears. Other clowns usually favour cold cream as a base for whitening – it certainly has a more bearable smell - but the tallow has greater lasting power and there will be little time for any touching up this evening.

With infinite care the clown measures a quantity of oxide chloride of bismuth out of a bottle into a tin cup and dabs it lightly on top of the tallow base with a piece of cotton wadding until every inch of exposed flesh is covered and his entire head is white. He then dips a fresh piece of wadding into a small pot of prepared chalk and pats it carefully all over the bismuth. The finished effect is truly dazzling, the combination of bismuth and chalk creating a bright, white, countenance which will appear even more radiant beneath the strong gas chandeliers in the cirque.

The clown can now paint on his trademark facial features. Taking a small pot of bright red vermilion powder, he mixes a minute quantity of it with a spoonful of liquefied tallow which has been melted over a candle. He then dips a fine, camel's hair brush into the mixture and, leaning closer into the looking glass, carefully paints triangles onto his cheeks and a grossly exaggerated 'cupid's bow' smile across his mouth. After repeating the mixing process with fine, sooty lampblack instead of vermilion, he draws on some narrow, arched eyebrows and a three-inch vertical black line over the middle of each eyelid. For a finishing touch, a spot of red ochre is applied to his chin with a soft hare's foot, and all that is needed is to fix his wig with spirit gum and adjust his costume. It is a well-practised regime, taking less than fifteen minutes. Where sat a plain acrobat now sits a veritable Prince of Laughter.

Meanwhile, William Hayes and his wife have entered the circle on horseback, another white-face clown running alongside them urging "Hup-la, allez!". It's clear the audience find this lively fellow naturally hilarious, but as 'clown to the horse' he knows there's more required of him than purely massaging funny-bones. He's already helped set up the arena and brought on armfuls of banners and hoops with jovial, feigned clumsiness. Now he has to stay out of range of the horse's hooves while ribbing the ringmaster and the riders and keeping the action flowing.

When William Hayes takes an unscheduled tumble it is a quick, impromptu gag by the clown which bridges the uncomfortable gap between shock and amusement.

After just a short break Wallett is due to make another appearance and as he enters the ring the departing clown bravely takes a pot shot at the jester's penchant for Shakespeare. "Why, what are a lovely woman's sparkling eyes?" offers the clown, fluttering his eyelashes, "Compared with Mrs Cannell's mutton pies!" With a roar, the ringmaster flicks his whip at the clown who scuttles out as the crowd dissolve with laughter.

They soon sense a change of mood, however, for Wallett does not begin straightaway but walks slowly around the ring fence looking closely at the people in the front row. Shortly he hesitates in front of a woman holding a baby girl wrapped in a shawl. After some whispered words the woman passes him the child and watches with tears in her eyes as he recites a well-known Lancastrian poem while walking around the ring with the babe in his arms. It's a long, sentimental piece, recognised by many of the audience and delivered in such a rich, colourful dialect that they're deeply touched. Even the child seems completely mesmerised and remains quiet until he's finished. But it's almost a relief when, after the next acrobatic display, it is a white-faced Clown who cartwheels into the ring with a gay "Here we are again!" and launches straight into a frenetic stream of patter.

In the sharp lights of the cirque this clown is truly a sight to behold. On his head he wears a wig that is a clear travesty of a jester's cap, the hair being divided into three sections made up of two tightly-curled sidepieces separated by a centre piece grotesquely oiled and teased into a giant cockscomb. The rest of his appearance, from his bright, eerie make-up to his long pointed pumps, is more of a parody on the powdered face and overblown frills of an Elizabethan courtier. His white cotton doublet has a deeply ruffled white collar, puffed shoulders and long, tight sleeves lavishly trimmed with braid. The fitted bodice has a deep peplum and is extravagantly embroidered and spangled with spots, diamonds and four-leafed clovers in green, red and blue. On his bottom half he wears capacious pumpkin breeches over striped canions tied at the knee with long gaudy ribbons and white tights embroidered with green and red flowers. The whole outfit is alive with puffs, frills, ribbons and ruffles.

Sadly, though, this Clown's humour begins and ends with his costume for his wheezes are entertaining only in their awfulness. A stream of ditties about holidaymakers is quickly followed by a series of unoriginal conundrums. "Why is the bell of St Matthew's like a good story? Because it is often tolled. Tolled, sir, do you see? Tolled. It's all in the way you hold your mouth."

The audience rumbles and groans and after an endless stream of tired, old jokes they break into a loud barrage of boo-ing, catcalls and hissing. As the Clown cowers under the raucous goosing the ringmaster takes it upon himself to usher him out of the ring while, just as quickly, ushering in a new assortment of buffos. This comical band is greeted with vigorous cheering and whistles. They had better be good.

'How!' calls a figure dressed in a Pierrot costume. 'Do!' says a second, ordinary white clown. 'You!' shrieks a third and 'Do!' shouts a fourth, as they leap, tumble and stilt-walk onto the sawdust. Before the audience have time to answer, a variety of props come flying out from behind the ring curtain - long strings of sausages, feather dusters, a pair of clogs, a trombone, a fiddle and a broom. Two more clowns then stagger in and out with a basket of carrots, buckets of water, a small cloth-covered table and a bottle of wine. This is more like it. The audience recognise the scene's potential for fun and burst into guffaws of laughter that echo round the ring as one of the clowns trips, lands with a thud and douses another with water. Another backs into the ringmaster and falls over, before somersaulting backwards and springing up over the ring fence, causing a group of young women on the front row to screech with fright.

The following few minutes offer up a seemingly random medley of merriment. Led by the elegant Pierrot in his conical hat, well-fitted white costume and tasteful ruff, and watched silently by a balletic Harlequin in black mask and sleek, multi-coloured spangles, one of the buffos struggles to set up the table and then pours the wine till it overflows, two others play a clever duet on the fiddle, another, for the benefit of the Lancastrians in the audience, dances a hornpipe while wearing clogs and the remainder engage in mock hand-to-hand combat with the sausages, carrots and feather dusters. Occasionally Harlequin intervenes and attempts to magically transform objects by hitting them with his slapstick, but he always ends up spinning away around the circle in a series of deft flips and somersaults.

They're a decidedly disparate bunch. Pierrot is clearly in charge and Harlequin dazzles in both style and agility but the others are a hotchpotch of the long and lanky, short and tubby and small and wiry, all dressed in multi-hued tights, frilled and spotted trunks, jingling bells and elongated pumps. And oh, how they love a good scuffle. The clowns' limbs fly and flail as they bump and knock against one another with genuine force. They are cuffed, boxed, sat upon, walloped and punched, ducking and diving, darting and tumbling, all the while grunting, laughing, singing and belly-aching. The action only concludes when a comic policeman enters the ring urging them to move on and is taunted by a clown. The policeman is glum and deadly serious, driving the audience to even greater laughter.

Once they've retreated to the dressing room the clowns fall about with real exhaustion. Mugs of beer are consumed to ease their raw throats, arnica is applied to bruised limbs and they're quick to wipe away their thick layers of face whitening. Harlequin is helped to peel out of his costume and his relief is immediate. The suit is decorated with thousands of bright spangles and weighs as hot and heavy as a suit of chainmail. A close inspection reveals that a dozen or so spangles have been torn off in the clowns' rough and tumble and Harlequin settles into a well-lit corner of the dressing room to fix them, wrapped in a warm dressing gown, armed with needle and thread. Fortunately, he has good eyes. The spangles are tiny, each one a flat, circular piece of coloured copper with a hole in the centre, sewn by hand onto triangular patches of fabric in single blocks of red, green, yellow and blue to represent the elements of fire, earth, air and water. When illuminated by the brilliant lights of the circus, they shimmer like the scales of a salmon caught in a rainbow.

Out in the circle it is once again the turn of Wallett to thrill the crowd with his own sharp brand of satire and comic philosophy. This time it's local events that have sparked his imagination and nothing is spared – the new vogue for swimming, a band of card sharpers who've been fleecing unwary visitors, the 'odious' new tuppenny tax on passengers sailing from the New Landing Pier and, most fun of all, the valiant efforts of Mr Poplin, the champion Island pedestrian, who's recently walked fifty miles in nine and a half hours, taking breakfast and dinner along the way. As Wallett himself describes it, his monologue is a comic's view on matters and things in general, and generally on things that don't matter.

He concludes by reciting a witty poem on one of his favourite subjects – the state of marriage. It's a light-hearted yet moral sentiment which appeals greatly to the adults in the audience but the children wriggle with boredom and once Wallett has left the circle it's left to the knockabout clowns to again inject some physical fun into the proceedings. Fortunately, their chaotic burlesque strikes all the right notes. All the usual clowning favourites are employed – the ubiquitous red-hot poker, plenty of thieving and pick-pocketing, bags of dirty laundry and wash tubs – and by the end a pile of clowns are heaped in the centre of the sawdust, spattered with soot, flour and squashed tomatoes. The fierce winds that have battered the tent all night are suddenly secondary to the vibrations created by a thousand bodies convulsing with laughter.

The evening is almost over. All that remains is one last curtain call by the great Wallett and as he enters the circle for the last time the audience grow silent in anticipation. They're rewarded with an ascerbic parting shot at the Island's unseasonal weather and as a ripple of mirth crescendoes from the pit to the highest points of the gallery Wallett gives the audience a long, low bow and takes his leave with thunderous applause ringing in his ears. He can just make out the ringmaster reminding the crowd that 'tonight is Mr Wallett's Benefit Night' and a few extra coins in the collection buckets on the way out would be greatly appreciated.

In the dressing room the other clowns have cleared a small space for Wallett to enjoy receiving visitors and the first to enter is his wife who watched the show from the front row with their young son Russell and baby daughter Florence. The little girl has already been round the cirque tonight in Wallett's arms but in the privacy of his dressing room he takes her into his arms again and kisses and fusses her as only a father can. Russell appears very at home amongst the boisterous clowns and smiles widely when they ruffle his hair and pinch his cheeks. The table is laden with gifts and flowers that have been left for his father and once Mrs Wallett and the children have retired to their lodgings the 'Queen's Jester' settles to sharing a bottle of champagne and plate of oysters with William Hayes. Ticket sales were splendid according to Mr Hayes and Wallett will do well with his share of the takings.

Before Wallett leaves the cirque one of the clowns stops to bid him goodnight. Stripped of his motley he's an ordinary looking man in a tired-looking linen suit and drab overcoat finished with wide astrakhan collar and cuffs. Only the show of heavy gold pins, rings and chains glinting about his person hint that he's a successful professional. His complexion is red and coarse from the daily rubbing to remove his face paint and his chin is already showing a dark shadow that will need a close shave before his next performance. It seems hard to believe that only hours ago this mundane fellow was an energetic vehicle for pranks and wheezes.

Wallett returns to his lodgings and a light supper with his wife, followed by brandy and a large cigar. His beloved children are tucked up in bed and he watches their dear faces sleeping for a while before closing the door. His little lad is already showing the makings of a performer and it brings joy to his old heart.

Outside, the wind is still blowing but not as fiercely and he's already looking forward to his next sea journey. It doesn't do to stay in one place too long.

He may retire in the near future. Or then again, he may not. The world of comedy is still open to exploration and new adventures and as long as the people of the Isle of Man are happy to welcome 'the Great W.F.Wallett' with open arms, he will be happy to entertain them.

Addendum

In 1872 William Wallett appeared before magistrates in Coventry charged with inciting a breach of the peace, after allegedly insulting a female member of the audience. It appeared that Mr Wallett had taken a dislike to Coventry's chief of police and, on spying the policeman's daughter in the audience, had berated her in a loud voice. The magistrates dismissed the charge but admitted they found his language improper and shocking. Such incidents didn't dint his career, however. In the 1880s, well into his seventies, he was still performing on the Isle of Man to crowded houses, bearing only a slight stoop and still displaying plenty of humour. Wallett died on the 13th March 1892 from pneumonia following an attack of influenza. He was eighty-five. Amongst many of the stories that surrounded him was that he was the oldest of twenty children and originally became clown in a pantomime at Sheffield. But it was generally agreed that he was without equal in his chosen profession and there was none more highly esteemed. On his death a committee was formed to raise subscriptions to place a monument over his grave and provide money for his widow.

William Hayes and Nat Emmett went on to enjoy adventurous careers. By 1878 Hayes was noted performing at the Great International Circus in Wanganui, New Zealand. Emmett headed to America.

In the 1870s English and American newspapers noted the tragic consequences of clown make up. Bismuth, ceruse and other forms of white lead were described as paralysis, heart disease and death in disguise. Bismuth in particular was linked to the deaths by insanity of several clowns.

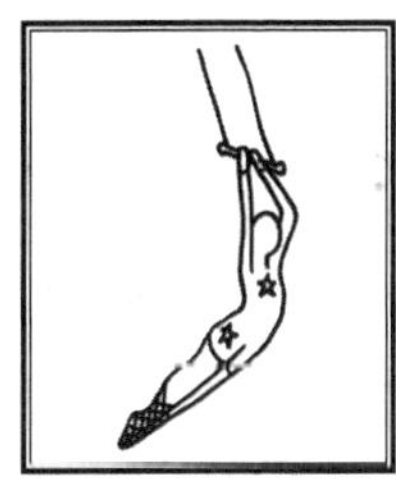

Chapter Nine

THE GLITTERING STAR

1880 Saturday 17th July

The young man is lying in the bath with his eyes closed, his forehead crystalline with beads of sweat. His body is immersed up to his neck in near-scalding water that has filled the room with steam and his pale shoulders are barely visible beneath the misty surface. As his head lolls back, his long, dark curly hair floats on the water like seaweed and pinpricks of light glint off the small gold hoops in his ears. He is utterly still and could be taken for dead if it weren't for the small, twitching smile that suggests he is merely dreaming.

It's seven o'clock in the morning and the young man has come early to the Aquarium Baths in Victoria Street to ease his taut muscles and allow his mind a precious hour in which to wander uncluttered, free from the usual constant pressures of circus life. As the hour progresses, he feels the heat seep into his aching joints and every now and then he squeezes his hands into tight fists and rolls his shoulders. Eventually he calls for the attendant to bring his towels and steps out of the bath to dress for the day ahead. His limbs feel pleasantly heavy and lethargic, and the dull pain so noticeable in his neck of late appears to have melted away.

Although it's mid-summer the morning air is still cool and the man covers his slim frame with three layers of clothing to prevent a chill. Checked trousers and jacket with crimson velvet vest adorned with a heavy gold watch chain, a double-breasted woollen overcoat with a wide collar, and a voluminous cloak tied with a gold pin in the shape of a horseshoe. The steam has crimped his hair into tight, corkscrew ringlets and he ties it back with a thin silk ribbon, before jamming on a tall, narrow-brimmed felt hat embellished with pheasant feathers. Prior to leaving the baths he checks his appearance in a looking glass and sets the hat on a jaunty angle. Staring back at him is a confident young man with sharp features, wide nostrils and large, pale-coloured eyes. He's only twenty-nine years old but looks, and feels, a good deal older.

Joe Smith, born in Essex in a travelling circus and known professionally as Joseph Ohmy, is a man of many talents who has spent the last ten years travelling around Europe and England under the guise of horse rider, clown, gymnast and company manager. But his real domain is in the air. Rope is to Joe what a pen is to a writer or a knife to a butcher. Flying trapeze, corde volante, slack wire – aerial gymnastics of the most daring and novel kind are his bread and butter. Lately he's been organising summer galas in Southport – worthy but dull - and the invitation to appear briefly at Charlie Keith's Circus in Douglas, just across the water, proved hard to resist. While reluctant to leave his wife Diana and their three lively toddlers at home Charlie is Joe's brother-in-law, a natural funny-man and one of England's most innovative circus proprietors. If the name Charlie Keith tops a playbill, audiences can be assured of a programme spiced with thrills and novelty.

On leaving the Baths Joe lifts his nose to the ozone-sharp tang of the sea, just a hundred yards from where he stands. Victoria Street is a wide, new commercial avenue that connects upper Douglas to the smart, well-organised promenades that now line the bay, by-passing the overcrowded old town in the process. Despite the early hour, Joe can already see dozens of bathing vans lined up along the shoreline waiting to take dippers into the bracing blue waters. Higher up the sloping beach, on banks of pebbles, laundry maids from the seaside boarding houses have stretched their freshly washed linen out to dry and, in the distance, the booths on the Iron Pier stand ready and waiting to take money off carefree summer visitors.

From now until sunset this part of town will buzz with activity. On every corner young lads are calling out the latest news headlines or polishing the boots of passing gentlemen. Throughout the day the new Douglas Bay horse tram service will transport hundreds of holidaymakers between the terraced guest houses and the steamers that lie in the harbour; dozens of cabs will hustle for the business of those visitors who are staying further out of town, and bill-stickers will post up the myriad of entertainments on offer in town, the circus amongst them. Douglas in the summer of 1880 has a vibrancy and confidence that Joe finds very appealing. It reminds him a lot of Southport. It smells and feels like a good place to be.

For now, though, he doesn't have the time to linger and enjoy the scene before him. His rehearsal is set for ten o'clock this morning and while Charlie may be his friend and brother-in-law he is also a stickler for discipline and time keeping. Lateness for a rehearsal or performance incurs a stiff fine, family or not.

Turning left, Joe heads up Victoria Street towards Upper Church Street and the grand new circus building which fronts onto the road, opposite St George's Church. A few years ago, having heard how Douglas was developing for the holiday market, Charlie did attempt to secure some plots down by the sea but the plans came to nothing and he's had to settle for the same site used by Hengler's and Hayes & Harvey in recent years. Still, the Island now boasts its own steam railway system and the main Douglas station is only a few hundred yards from the circus, which bodes well for attracting crowds from out of town.

As with anything that Charlie does, this building has been planned and executed to his own exacting standards. Even if they are dictated more by finance than an eye for quality. Most of his profits are sunk into his buildings – this one cost just short of a thousand pounds - and he usually has more than one on the go at any one time. Last year, he had to build a total replacement for his circus in Derby after it burnt to the ground one dreadful night, in which the lives of a young groom and twenty valuable horses were lost, along with a quantity of valuable equipment. And even as this season in the Isle of Man got underway he was already thinking ahead to the coming winter season and the circus he is building in Wigan to maintain his presence in the north. Charlie may only be a small man but he has the dynamism of a giant.

Fifteen minutes after leaving the Baths Joe enters the Church Street circus via the lower pit entrance. It is a formidable building constructed of wood and iron and by night up to two thousand people will congregate inside its lavishly furnished, papered and panelled interior and sweat beneath the lights. By day, however, it is cold, dark and oppressive. The cavernous auditorium is empty apart from a single rider putting her horse through its paces in the ring under the whip of the equestrian director. The girl is young and in the shadowy light she appears plain and ordinary, her mount an equally plain mare unadorned except for thin streaks of white foam on its dark coat. As Joe makes his way through to the property room the sound of voices gradually builds and bodies spill from every door. The area behind the auditorium is a maze of offices, dressing rooms, stables and exercise yards and every corner is occupied by someone at work.

Before ten o'clock he needs to check his equipment and ensure it is in full working order. It's one of the most important tasks of his day and must be carried out with a clear head. All of the ropes, bars, fixings and safety net are his own property but it will require a number of men to rig them correctly and he needs to be sure everyone knows what they are doing.

In the property room he speaks first to the head property man. In its transportable state his safety net is a huge, heavy bundle which, when unrolled, will measure about seventy feet long and forty feet wide. It consists of a large meshed net made of twisted cotton yarn, bound on each side with heavy ropes and entirely covered with a thin carpet. A system of stays and guides around the edges will secure the ends, sides and corners to fixings in the auditorium, covering the entire ring. Safety nets have only found their way into the circus in the past few years. It's said that they originated on French building sites to protect workmen falling from great heights but they underline the acrobat's paradox - a performer whose safety is properly ensured can achieve ever more daring and dramatic feats. Not that Joe always gets the chance to use a net. When he performs in theatres and music halls he's usually flying over the audience and there is only room for a mattress on the stage to break your fall.

In the early days of his career Joe performed mostly on the static trapeze – a thin wooden bar fixed between two poles – but in recent years he's become well practised on the flying trapeze, the act invented by the French gymnast Jules Leotard, in which the wooden bar is attached to ropes suspended from the ceiling. Tonight, for the first part of his performance he will swing through the air on the flying trapeze with the safety net below to catch him if he falls. In the second part, during which he will attempt his daring 'Fall for Life' from the high corde volante, the net will be removed.

Joe and Charlie have had many conversations recently about the public's desire for ever more sensational acts. A dance upon a slack wire is no longer enough to satisfy the appetite for morbid entertainment. Even the relatively new flying trapeze seems to be already found dull by those thrill-seekers who hunger for tricks imbued with imminent danger. Charlie often says that a man who hopes to make his way in the ring nowadays must be the master of the clever novelty. The joy of Joe's act is that it combines breath-taking excitement with the beauty and grace of flying. His poetically titled yet visually shocking 'Fall For Life' should fit the bill nicely.

At midday he joins Charlie, his sister Lizzie – Charlie's wife - and many of the other artistes for dinner, taken at a long table set up outside in the stable yard. Joe eats frugally, a little cheese, salad vegetables and fruit, washed down with nothing stronger than tea. Like many of his gymnastic colleagues he abstains from alcohol. Not only does it thicken the waist but he's seen what accidents can happen when it clouds the brain. Plus, drunkenness during working hours in a Charlie Keith Circus is liable to lose you a night's salary.

The talk at the table is lively and interspersed with exotic phrases and anecdotes. Charlie, after years of travelling, is proficient in Russian, French, German and Spanish but there is also a good smattering of the colourful language used by circus people. Joe will often refer to his wife as a 'dona' and the money in his pocket as 'denarlies', terms unrecognised by 'gajos' or outsiders but readily understood by everyone in the ring no matter where they hail from.

After the initial banter the company are keen to swap stories of their dare-devil exploits and Charlie urges Joe to recount the time in Paris when he was touted as 'The

Hero of the Balloon', performing his 'Flight for Life'. Ah, now, that was a crowd puller!

At an outdoor fête, Joe recalls, as visitors enjoyed a variety of entertainments a giant balloon in a side field was filled with gas, a process that took about four and a half hours. Once the balloon was filled a basket was attached and, while still tethered to ground ropes, the balloon was allowed to ascend high enough for Joe to sit on a trapeze bar suspended from the basket. To the sound of the cheering crowd the balloon was then loosed from its guy ropes and allowed to float free. As the balloon gained height he let go and fell backwards to hang by his knees, then dropped further to his ankles, before swinging up to grab the bar with his hands and dangle carelessly as though within touching distance of solid ground. Gradually the balloon flew higher and higher and Joe's performance only terminated when the balloon was a mere pinprick in the sky, at which point he nonchalantly clambered back up into the basket and steered the balloon to its landing point about eight miles away. The public were enamoured and appalled by the act in equal measure. Indeed, the start of another flight was almost delayed by a young man barging through the crowd to reach him, only to hand Joe his business card – that of a local undertaker!

Around the table, the story prompts an outburst of laughter and shaking of heads. Charlie claps his hands to indicate the midday meal is over and Joe retires to his lodgings for a short nap.

Even the sounds of Douglas at the height of the season are not enough to prevent Joe sleeping the sleep of the dead and by two o'clock he is ready to return to the circus to go through a series of gymnastic exercises in the yard. Working on the trapeze requires a fit, supple body and for half an hour he practises slow, gentle, repetitive movements to stretch and strengthen his arms and shoulders. He then finds a quiet doorway with a sturdy frame and uses it to pull himself up ten, twenty, thirty times. After the briefest pause he drops to the floor and performs a hundred push ups, grunting only towards the end. It's a routine so ingrained that he hardly has to think about it. From the time he was two years old, travelling from town to town with his father's circus, Joe was always an active child, inherently plucky and agile, and his actress mother and large brood of acrobatic sisters often teased him into jumping higher, leaping further and running harder. The next step - to performing - felt as natural as breathing and soon his only obligations were those dictated by show times. Now, as he prepares to entertain the people of Douglas, he is thankful that the trapeze has not only helped him to develop a sharp mind and a healthy body, but enabled him to escape the mantle of drudgery worn so heavily by those who watch him with awe and envy.

As the other acts complete their rehearsals Joe personally supervises the rigging of the trapeze platforms, ladders, ropes and bars and the corde volante, checking every knot, cord, nut and bolt. It is a careful and precise, almost mathematical procedure requiring every ounce of his concentration and focus. Measurements must be exact and minute attention is paid to the equipment. Small patches of rust are rubbed off the metal fittings with steel wool, seals and splices are checked for firmness, all surfaces of the rigging and platforms are assessed for damage and wiped over with damp cloths to remove any chalk residue. Most importantly, every inch of rope used in his act is thoroughly inspected for signs of wear and tear. The narrow trapeze ropes are made of tough, braided hemp and part of his act also incorporates a most unusual set of thick elastic ropes, made of hemp and India rubber. He regularly has them tested by a firm of engineers to ensure they can withstand at least six times his own weight but constant handling and varying conditions still take their toll. The length of the elastic ropes is particularly vital and halfway through the afternoon he calls for the auditorium to be emptied while he and his assistant undertake a test that must remain completely secret until his performance reveals all.

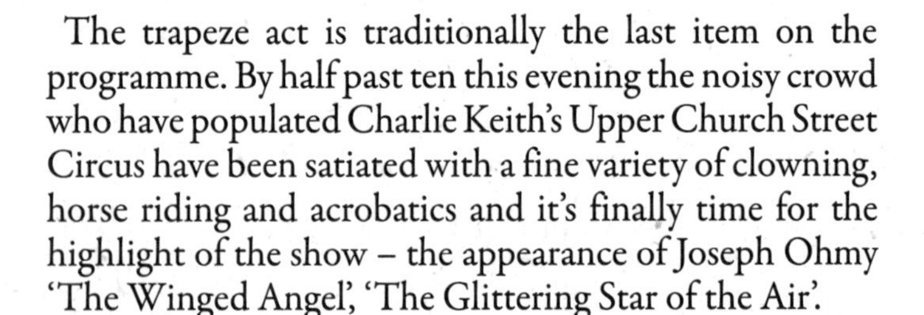

The trapeze act is traditionally the last item on the programme. By half past ten this evening the noisy crowd who have populated Charlie Keith's Upper Church Street Circus have been satiated with a fine variety of clowning, horse riding and acrobatics and it's finally time for the highlight of the show – the appearance of Joseph Ohmy 'The Winged Angel', 'The Glittering Star of the Air'.

Before Joe can take to the ring Charlie comes on dressed in his clown costume to distract the audience while the property master and his team bring on the giant safety net and large crates full of ropes and fixings. The band master urges his musicians into a gay repertoire of lively songs and Charlie gets the whole audience singing to drown out the noise of the net being hooked into place, though the very sight of it appears to drive some of the more excitable members of the crowd into a frenzy of anticipation. They're already craning their necks up to the trapeze platforms and attempting to conjure up the image of a man flying. Or falling. It is a disturbing, deeply thrilling vision.

In the performer's waiting area behind the main curtain Joe is warming up. For ten minutes he jumps on the spot, stretches and rolls his shoulders, then moves to the floor to do a short series of sit ups and push ups. Finally, when the manager's bell is rung, he takes a long drink from a pitcher of water, wipes his hands thoroughly on a dry towel and bounds through the curtain into the ring. The crowd rise to their feet and give him a thunderous welcome as he nimbly climbs a rope ladder until he is level with the net, then neatly tumbles onto it and uprights himself with a series of bounces that are part-show and part-test. To a drum roll from the band he hops back onto the ladder and climbs up to the high trapeze platform where he styles to the audience, hand outstretched, his wide smile clearly visible against the dark ceiling.

In the high vault of the building the gas chandeliers throw their bright white light over his small, svelte frame, making it immediately obvious why he calls himself 'The Glittering Star of the Air'. His jacket is magnificent – the close-fitting, dark velvet bodice is embroidered with large gold stars and edged with gold braid; wide shoulder epaulettes are embellished with more gold stars and trimmed with gold tassels, and the long plain sleeves end in deep velvet cuffs. On his feet he wears eye-catching calf-length, gladiatorial leather boots, striped in black and gold and laced to just below the knee. As the band strikes up a waltz and the audience settle into their seats, Joe removes his jacket and hooks it onto the scaffolding revealing star-covered trunks worn over a close fitting, one-piece thin woollen suit in the style of the great Leotard.

Far below, the audience tilt back their heads to follow his movements, unaware that some of the performers have slipped quietly from behind the curtain to join them in gazing upwards. It's a rare treat to be allowed to witness an act such as this and one of Charlie's few concessions. In the monster gallery at the back of the building over a thousand spectators focus their full attention on the tiny figure on the left-hand platform and hold their breath as he prepares to fly.

On the platform Joe dips his hands into a tub of chalk and rubs it over his palms and fingers, then, with all the grace of a dancer, steps onto the pedestal board and takes hold of the trapeze bar. With a shout of 'Hep!' he leaps into the air and soars across the arena, his body flexed and elongated, his toes perfectly aligned. On his return he curls up his legs and threads them over the bar so that he hangs by his knees, his hands flopping downwards. He then pulls himself up to a sitting position and lies backwards, legs extended, his whole body effortlessly horizontal. All the while the audience are staring upwards, open mouthed, eyes shining, swept up in the music and languid movements of this half-man, half-monkey.

After a few more flights and a variety of contortions he returns to the pedestal board and poses for a few seconds to acknowledge the inevitable applause. Across the void on the other platform his assistant is waiting, holding a second trapeze bar and their eyes meet as Joe prepares to leap again. Their mutual trust is crucial. Timing and co-ordination are everything. A moment after Joe jumps the assistant lets go of the second bar and allows it to swing across the dark space between them. As the two bars close together Joe releases his hold, spins in mid-air and for a single exhilarating instant hovers, floating unsupported and un-tethered before grabbing the second bar and swinging across to the right-hand platform. Far below, the audience draw a single breath and the band increase their tempo. Never has dicing with death appeared so graceful or so full of joy.

Safely back on the first platform Joe applies more chalk to his hands, rubs some onto the trapeze bar and leaps once again into the air. But something is amiss. As he reaches for the second trapeze he is just an inch or two short and the audience gasp in horror with shouts of 'No!' as he plunges towards the net. Even now an awkward fall could break his neck. Hitting the heavy side ropes could break his back. But one of the first things instilled into him as a boy was the importance of a good landing. With remarkable composure he twists his body in mid-air so that his head is facing downwards and relaxes, like a tumbler pigeon, into a slow somersault, landing perfectly on his back, head tucked in, in the middle of the net. The deep bounce immediately rights him to his feet, and he smiles and waves to the relieved audience who call his name, shouting for him to continue. Which he does, scuttling up the ladder with the same unwavering confidence and even more bravado.

What follows is a magical, exhilarating sequence of aerial acrobatics comprising single somersaults, double somersaults and elegant contortions conducted in a blur of twirling stars and stripes. In time to the music he hangs by his knees and ankles; floats and glides like a bright, golden angel and pirouettes in a rush of air that makes the glass chandeliers tinkle. It's a heart-stopping display of extraordinary style, timing and agility and the audience are spellbound. To finish this section of his act, he treats them to one final show of daring, his bold 'leap for life'. Across the arena the single rope of the corde volante hangs slackly between two high posts and, to a drum roll from the band below, Joe swings across the space on his trapeze, gradually building momentum until, with one final push, he hurls himself from the trapeze bar, somersaults through the air and catches the corde volante, fifteen feet away, where he hangs for a few seconds before dropping lightly to the safety net. The precision and courage of this bold, flawless movement drives the crowd to a barrage of whistling, clapping and calls of 'oh-my, oh-my!'

Joe is elated but hot, sweaty and parched. His wrists hurt and his shoulder muscles are tender. As the property men move into the circle to dismantle the net, he slips behind the ring curtain to sit a minute and gulp down numerous tankards of water. He has shown the audience the 'leap for life', now he feels the usual rush of adrenalin that always precedes his 'fall for life'. And it is adrenalin tinged with real fear for the rope nearly had him once. Caught around the neck he was nearly throttled to death and was only saved by a quick-thinking assistant and a sharp knife. The memory haunts him still.

Back in the ring, Charlie has called for silence, even from the band. This next and final trick by the one and only 'King Ohmy' defies all the laws of gravity and nature. In recent years, he tells the crowd, Christian missionaries have returned from the islands of the South Seas with tales of men who jump off high wooden towers with long twisted vines attached to their ankles. They do it to show they are men of courage, to display their faith in nature and to bless their crops. Now, today, right here in the Isle of Man there is amongst us a young man of equal courage who will put his own life on the line to demonstrate an ancient tradition such as they have never seen before!

Joe re-enters the ring to an ominous hush. In the unusual silence, and without the net, the cirque seems suddenly vast and oppressive, and he appears strangely small and helpless. Nervous coughs break out as he climbs up to the corde volante, loosely strung about forty feet above the heads of the audience in the pit. With practised ease he settles himself comfortably in the centre of the rope and bends to check something at his ankles. He then stands, wavering slightly but holding the rope firmly on either side, and, using his body to create a gentle motion, begins to swing over the audience. The rhythm of the corde volante starts out smooth, eerily slow and unhurried and it gives those who are willing to keep looking upwards a better view of Joe's sinewy physique. At this distance he appears to be all muscle, with not an extra ounce of flesh, the tendons standing out on his strong arms and shoulders, the bones of his face sharp and chiselled.

As he builds up speed and momentum, the rope begins to create a swishing sound that rushes through the roof of the building. Even the iron fixings can be heard to creak as they strain against the movement. With Joe's shadow sweeping over them in ever greater arcs the audience struggle to remain silent, groaning in morbid anticipation and averting their eyes. Faster and faster he goes, the draught loosening the silk ribbon that binds his long hair so that his dark curls fall forward around his face, only to be blown back again as he soars upwards, the ceiling coming within touching distance of his striped boots.

And then comes a moment imbued with such incredulity that afterwards it will be replayed over and over in the minds of those who witness it to try and recapture what really happened. As he begins a downward swing Joe appears to lose his grip on the cord and falls forward, arms outstretched. Directly beneath him in the fourth row of the pit women and children scream in horror, their eyes transfixed on his plummeting body, their limbs frozen with shock. Ten feet he plunges, head first, hair streaming behind him, twenty feet, thirty feet. For a few terrifying seconds time stands still. And then. Boof!

With just a couple of feet to spare between his head and those of the audience two elastic cords attached to Joe's ankles brutally cut short his descent, snapping him back into the air in a wide somersault that flips him over and lands him in the ring. In the gallery, where a clear view has lent the audience an insight into the mechanics of the trick, a stunned silence is followed by deafening applause, while in the pit directly beneath his flight path hysterical women gather up their children and scramble over each other in their haste to get away.

In the ring, the performer is on his feet, bent over and breathing deeply, his palms pressed against his thighs. His face is obscured by his damp curls but then he raises one hand to acknowledge that he is still in one piece.

'Oh my!' say the audience to one another, 'oh my!'

Addendum

In September 1884, Joe Ohmy seriously injured his back while performing his 'fall for life' at the Blackpool Winter Gardens. Ohmy struck the platform below and although no bones were broken he was severely bruised and shocked. Not that it curtailed his career. In 1903 he performed as a 'Human Rocket' at his circus in Wigan, diving from the roof to the ground in a blaze of fireworks.

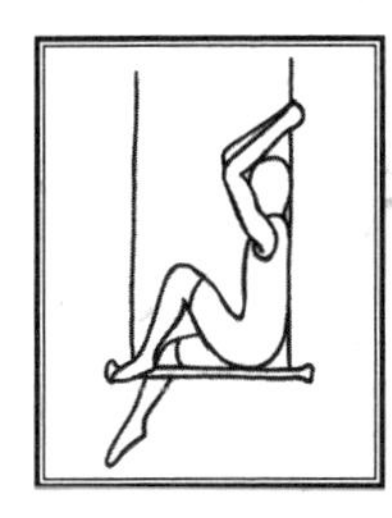

Chapter Ten

THE FLYING WONDER

1880 Monday 27th September

The man in the corner of the gymnast's dressing room appears intent on his hands. For the last half hour he's been soaking them in a bucket of dark yellow, ammonia-scented urine and they smell bad, really bad. It's an old, aerialist's trick to toughen and heal the skin and all the male performers at Charlie Keith's Circus have cheerfully contributed to the bucket's contents. When trapeze artists are on the programme it's a standing joke that the dressing rooms smell riper than a lavatory.

Aside, however, from the unfortunate smell which pervades the air around him, this artist – the Great Artois - is a magnificent specimen of mankind. Five feet eight inches in his stockinged feet, blonde haired, with a fair complexion and heavy blonde moustache, he is as solid as a barn door. Sitting in his undershirt and drawers the rock-hard muscles of his broad chest, shoulders and stomach are clearly evident beneath his thin garments, his arms and legs as firm and sturdy as table legs. The only impediments to his fine limbs are patches of thick, leathery skin, hidden from view on the back of his knees.

His hands, also, are remarkable. Strong and square with large knuckles. Few of his colleagues will risk a handshake for fear of his iron grip. And his palms are curiously ribbed with hard, raised patches of dull, thickened skin. When he started out sixteen years ago, before he learned how to grip the bar properly, no amount of chalk could prevent him developing blisters on a daily basis but with time and care they were eventually replaced by tough calluses. It was a painful rite of passage but well worth persevering. These scar-like ridges are his 'badge of honour', worn with the pride of a seasoned aerialist.

Today he has to pay special attention to them. Lately he's allowed his skin to become dry, and friction from the trapeze bar has ripped off some of the protective layer. If he isn't careful it will make for an uncomfortable performance.

After washing his hands clean of the stale urine, he removes small particles of chalk residue out of the rips and dabs them with tincture of benzoin, the fragrant resin from the Spice Islands that smells like fermented oranges but stings like fire. He then gently rubs sandpaper over the remaining calluses to smooth their edges and opens a tub of thick white lotion to massage into his skin. Sometimes, if his children - Ellen, Alfred and John – are with him they'll fight over who's going to help him rub in the lotion. It's a well-meaning idea that usually ends in chaos, the children laughing and spattered with white spots or gathered by their father into a big, slippery bear hug.

The children know their father as John Lilley but tonight, under the roof of Charlie Keith's Circus, in the last days of the summer season, he will take to the ring as 'Monsieur Artois, the Flying Gymnast'.

John and Charlie are already well acquainted, having toured together only last year, although, unfortunately for John, he was in Derby when Charlie's circus was ravaged by fire, sending his expensive safety net, costumes and rigging up in smoke. While he's replaced most things, he still can't afford a new net, which ironically has lent his act an element of danger that was previously lacking and has subsequently doubled his worth. Charlie is usually good to pay though and John's good looks, star quality and sensational performance should provide just the finale that Charlie is looking for.

As a special treat for the people of Douglas, he also decides that all ladies shall be admitted free. A stampede could be in order.

'Monsieur Artois' is ready. Dressed in a skin-tight tunic and white tights with green facings sprinkled with silver stars, he is every inch a shining orb in the cosmos, radiating confidence and panache. The audience is full to bursting, mostly with pink-cheeked ladies of all ages and sensibilities. In the heat of the circus they flutter their fans and unbutton their jackets to ease their discomfort.

From the second he enters the ring Artois immediately has their rapt attention. Beginning with a mesmerising ground performance on the horizontal bars he then ascends to the great heights of the flying trapeze, wooing his audience with leaps, dives, somersaults and twirls. He hangs by his knees, by his feet, by his ankles, bending the crowd to his will, making them gasp, moan, 'ooh' and 'aah'.

Halfway through his allotted time he even leaps twenty-five feet in mid-air through suspended hoops, catching a stationary trapeze bar on the other side with one hand. Occasionally, he pretends to fall and the great swathe of Oriental fans beneath him flap with renewed vigour. With no net to catch him, the scent of danger is tangible and at times his performance is almost unbearable to watch.

But that is the view from the ground. In the air John Lilley is invincible. High up in the roof of the circus he is master of his own small universe. No debt collectors or irate landlords can reach him here. As he flies his whole body is flooded with the most intense sensations. The freedom of a bird as it glides through the sky, the weightlessness of a fish as it floats through water. It is little short of glorious. In all his experience of gymnastics there is nothing to match it.

After a time he's no longer even aware of the pain in his hands. The passion that first stirred his soul sixteen years ago is re-ignited with every sweep through the air. He feels extraordinarily elated, clear-headed and curiously safe. His body is tossed aloft, his strong hands are braced against the elements. With nothing below him and nothing above, he is flying. And nothing else matters.

Addendum

Two years after his appearance on the Isle of Man John Lilley wrote to the Star Music Hall in Dublin seeking a two-week engagement on the flying trapeze for £7 per week. One evening, while performing high above the stage he made a fatal error of judgement, fell thirty feet to the boards below and fractured his skull. He died almost instantly.

At the inquest, at which he was described as one of the finest illustrators of his art in Europe, his widow Sarah was distraught. They had been battling poverty, she said, ever since Lilley's equipment was destroyed in a fire and he was constantly working to get himself out of debt. Losing the best of husbands had left her with three young children and just four pounds to her name.

The family struggled on and Sarah eventually re-married, while her sons Alfred and John found work in the printing and iron trades.

However, thrill-seeking was in their blood. In the early twentieth century Alfred and John Lilley took to the air as clowning trapeze artistes, electrifying audiences with their clever and comical act - 'The Brothers Artois'.

Chapter Eleven

THE KING OF THE CANNON

1882 Friday 1st September

Posters are everywhere in this town. They thickly paper walls and gables and shout their entertainments from placards and shop windows. No sooner has one fixture ended than it's pasted over with some new attraction – a concert, dance or minstrel show; a fête, fancy fair or bazaar. Theatrical dramas fight for space alongside firework displays, panoramas do battle with horticultural shows, balloon ascents compete with round-the-island steamer trips. At times there's such a barrage of words that most of the advertising barely rates a passing glance. But today there is a colourful poster pasted up in the market place which, by virtue of its bold illustration, has enticed half a dozen men to stop and take a closer look.

The picture shows a fine looking, heavily muscled, moustachioed man wearing red boots and a skimpy red leotard. His gloved hands are raised in front of him, as though ready for a catch, and his feet are in a braced position. The expression on his face is one of total concentration and focus. And so it should be, for flying straight towards him is a cannonball, graphically captured in mid-flight against a vivid orange flash and cloud of smoke. In the background, partly obscured by the smoke, is a man dressed in artillery uniform, standing behind the large-wheeled cannon from which the ball was fired.

The man in the leotard styles himself as 'Herr Holtum - the King of the Cannon', a strapping Danish-American who, according to the poster, has been impressing audiences worldwide for more than twenty years with his strength and extraordinary courage, his forte being the catching of a real cannonball. Tonight, following a fortnight of successful performances at Harmston's Circus in Douglas, he and his wife 'Fraulein Anna' will take their Benefit and, in a grandiose farewell gesture, Herr Holtum is prepared to issue two formidable, but potentially lucrative, challenges to the people of Douglas. Firstly, to any man who can provide two horses capable of pulling him away from a wooden frame, he is offering the extraordinary sum of one hundred pounds. Secondly, he is also prepared to give a hundred pounds to any man who can replicate his own feat of catching a flying cannonball. The prize for the second feat may equal the first but the kudos of such a win will be far greater.

The men ogling the poster exchange looks and badger each other to accept the second challenge until, reading on, they are brought up short. In the fine print at the bottom Herr Holtum warns of the heavy price that some previous challengers have paid. The details are sobering.

Four years ago, at Manchester, a young man had his right hand severely damaged. Shortly after, at Hastings, a shoulder was broken. In Grimsby serious injuries were sustained and, likewise, in Hull. Then, two years ago at Leeds, a market porter attempting to catch the cannonball leaned forward at just the wrong moment and took a direct blow to the forehead, fracturing his skull. The man lay unconscious for six days and six nights and, although he eventually came to, Herr Holtum was charged with unlawful wounding. By the grace of God the jury acquitted him but he has been paying his dues ever since - to the benefit of the Leeds Infirmary which nursed the poor shattered porter back from the brink.

Such statistics make grim reading and the men of Douglas pull their jackets tighter against a sudden chill. A hundred pounds would make them rich beyond their wildest dreams but who amongst them will risk being blown to pieces for such a prize?

Soren 'John' Holtum, meanwhile, is completely oblivious to the flurry of nervous excitement aroused by his posters. He is sitting in semi-darkness, in a small outhouse in Upper Church Street, humming to himself, crooning and ruminative. One hand is braced against the cold, black muzzle of a four-foot long siege cannon, the other polishes the cannon's smooth barrel with a large cloth. As he works he leans in closer, his eyes closed. In the harsh light of day his visage is as tough and rugged as a block of granite, his wide forehead, high cheekbones and angular jaw all pointing to his Nordic origins. Here, in the quiet, solitary, filtered light of the outhouse, his features are curiously softened by his affection for an inanimate lump of iron.

Holtum is thirty-seven-years old but still slim and muscular for his age and of finer proportions than your typical fairground strongman. When standing at full height he appears tall due to his upright frame and a thick, curly thatch of sandy-coloured hair. Aged just fifteen when he left Denmark for a new life in America, he worked his passage on a diet of hard tack and salt-horse, and learnt early that physical labour was the best school for honing the body. It's the damage to his hands that betrays the precarious nature of his more recent career. In places the skin is scarred and shiny, one hand is missing a finger and those that remain are gnarled and crooked, the result of having been broken and fixed in haste – or not fixed at all. And all because of an old piece of artillery that, according to his wife Anna, he loves more than his own children!

It's certainly true that the man and the gun are long-standing companions. It was twelve years ago while touring the music halls of the Black Country that he spotted the cannon in the yard of a Birmingham merchant. It was lying on the dirt floor, with no carriage or trail and unremarkable to look at – little more than a plain tube of cast iron – but it had clean, smooth lines and weighed in at a formidable sixteen hundred pounds, impossible to move by man alone. The merchant was willing to let him have it for five pounds and Holtum paid up straightaway.

It was only much later that he realised his unassuming weapon carried the hallmarks of a colourful past. On the top of the barrel he noted a double-headed eagle embossed into the metal and eventually discovered this to be the emblem of Imperial Russia, making it likely the cannon was one of the many Russian guns captured by the British during the Crimean campaign and later shipped to England as war trophies. The contradiction between its simple facade and its past role as a powerful engine of destruction still makes him shudder. If only it could talk, what conversations they would have!

Because the cannon had no carriage when Holtum bought it, his first task was to have a carriage manufactured incorporating large iron wheels and a solid cast iron mount on which to rest the barrel. He also recalls how he changed the firing mechanism of the gun from being a muzzle loader, wherein the ball is rammed down the barrel, to a breech loader, in which the ball and powder are loaded from the rear.

For the first eight months of their new relationship Holtum spent every day developing and practising his 'catching' act in total privacy until he felt confident enough to perform in public. Since then they have travelled together throughout England, Europe, America and the Far East, by mule train, ship and rail. They have appeared before the Czar of Russia, Germany's Prince Bismarck and General Grant in Copenhagen. They have thrilled, frightened, mystified, and yes, occasionally misfired, but, more than a decade on, their unusual double act still pulls in the crowds and fills his family's coffers.

The invitation to join Harmston's Circus for a fortnight couldn't have come at a better time - for both parties. The Holtum family were in need of work, having recently sold up their own small circus company, and Harmston's were looking to offer something a little meatier than their usual light-hearted fare of horses and clowns. Something to end the season with a bang. A mutual arrangement was reached and two weeks ago the Holtums parked up close to Charlie Keith's old circus building in Upper Church Street (now redecorated and refurbished with a striking new roof canopy of red and white stripes).

Their convoy certainly made an interesting sight as it rumbled up the hill. Holtum and his assistant drove ahead in the sombre and securely-bolted main wagon, four big dray horses straining to haul its heavy black cargo of cannon, cannonballs and metal canisters filled with black powder. Close behind, Anna followed in their brightly painted living wagon, their two children, six year old Alvira and four year old Oscar, squeezed in amongst a pile of props and costumes, a stock of large American picture posters and Anna's beloved performing dogs, a pampered brood of pugs and spaniels which yapped incessantly at passers-by. The steep sides of Upper Church Street are lined with busy taverns, shops and hotels, and dozens of curious shoppers, drawn by the noise, emerged onto the road to watch them pass by.

Now, a fortnight on, and in the last throes of what has been a highly successful Manx engagement, Holtum finishes cleaning and polishing his precious piece of artillery. With great care he covers it with a tarpaulin before locking up and making his way down Victoria Street to the Victoria Coffee Palace Hotel. Holtum doesn't touch alcohol, never has done, and during his time in Douglas he has become acquainted with the Blue Ribbon Army, a fervent bunch of tee-totallers who rail against the growing problem of inebriation in the town. One of those he converses with over a large glass of sarsaparilla is a big, tough looking fellow in his late thirties named Thomas Boyde, a former soldier who has himself experienced the more unpleasant side effects of drink. After being discharged from the army on just sixpence a day, Boyde tells Holtum, he found solace in rum and ale, until a pub brawl ended in a man's death and he found himself in the Castle lock-up. On his release, he took the pledge to forego drinking and has since become a Blue Ribbon stalwart, promoting their temperance cause with great zeal and energy.

Holtum leans forward as he listens to Boyde tell his tale. His hearing is limited – a legacy of years spent too close to cannon-fire – and when he replies to Boyde it is in thickly accented English with rolling vowels that make him sound as though he is sucking on a marble.

Three years after settling in San Francisco, he tells Boyde, he too saw a good deal of drunken behaviour while managing the refreshment department of a small theatre. But during that time he was offered the chance to take to the stage and it was a move he's never regretted. He started out on the slack wire and, from then on, tried everything that was thrown at him - gymnastics, clowning, acts of strength and juggling – leaving the theatre shortly afterwards to travel with a small circus through California's beer-soaked mining camps, then up to British Columbia and back down to Mexico.

A while later he travelled back across the Atlantic, met and married his wife Anna, purchased his cannon and began performing all over Europe. A series of lucrative engagements followed, including a particularly memorable one at the wild and colourful Folies Bergere in Paris where he was probably the only person who was sober!

His missing finger always invites questions and Holtum responds with a certain relish. The cannon, he explains, is an unforgiving companion. In the months before he first performed in public he would practise to the point of exhaustion. While still learning his craft this weariness led to a small miscalculation. The result was undoubtedly inconvenient but he has learned to adjust.

In the Victoria Hotel there's an awed silence as Holtum drains the last of his sarsaparilla and bids farewell to his new friends. A number of them plan to attend his evening performance and, as he ducks out into the rain and disappears back up Victoria Street in the direction of the circus, they wonder what dramas await them.

The audience at tonight's Benefit are a rowdy lot. Many of them have been sheltering from the wet and stormy afternoon in the town's numerous taverns, drinking and squabbling over cards and skittles. Several in the gallery are imbibing still, swigging furtively from ginger beer bottles filled with rum. The Brothers Rudolph have attempted to warm them up with a fine show of acrobatics but they're proving to be a difficult crowd, belligerent and agitated. When their attention is finally captured there comes a genuine gasp of shock. For they're introduced to the power of cannon fire not by a man, but a woman.

On a drum roll from the band, Fraulein Anna Holtum enters the ring, a small field cannon carefully balanced on one beefy shoulder. She's a striking-looking woman, oozing vitality, her short red hair and salacious tight red costume giving the impression of a human firework. Around her head she wears a thickly wound red scarf that covers her ears. Her arms and legs are as good as naked, shapely and toned, with biceps almost as big as her husband's. The audience buzzes with excitement until they are hushed into silence by the ringmaster. Anna turns the cannon to face away from the audience and a man steps up behind her with a small bag from which he pours gunpowder into the touch hole. He then lights it with a slow-burning match and stands well back, putting his hands over his ears and urging the audience to do the same. With a massive 'Boom!' a lump of wadding bursts from the cannon in a cloud of acrid smoke and the force of the blast rocks Fraulein Anna back on her heels. In a sudden burst of energy the audience are on their feet - let the Benefit begin!

At which point the real star of the moment enters the ring. Herr Holtum, The Cannonball King, bounds out onto the sawdust, resplendent in his customary red leather ankle boots and sleeveless red leotard, finished with a yellow belt and cut in a deep plunging v that shows off his broad, bare chest. To the crowd's initial disappointment, however, he appears to be in no rush to play with cannonballs. First, he must warm up his muscles and to do so he demonstrates an intriguing set of exercises using Indian clubs, the heavy wooden instruments popular with military cadets and gymnasiums for improving one's physique and posture.

Shaped like overgrown bowling pins, each club is two feet long, narrow at the handle end and widening towards the base. Holding one in each hand Holtum begins by gracefully swivelling the clubs in small circles, slowly building up to larger circles and diagonal movements that loop across his torso and over his shoulders. He then rises up on his toes and holds the clubs above his head, before swinging them in circles to the front and sides, like a slow, graceful dance. The weight of the clubs would quickly exhaust an ordinary man yet every movement by the big Dane is smooth and deliberate and has a neatness and finish that seems at odds with his rugged appearance.

As Holtum builds his rhythm he begins to swing the clubs in opposite directions, gaining speed until he suddenly finishes a large sweeping circle by striking the clubs on the ground. The noise is like a gunshot. Some of the younger members of the audience cry out and any chatter is swiftly silenced.

The move marks a change in the atmosphere that is almost brutal. Discarding the clubs Holtum asks for a new set of instruments to be brought into the ring. The clubs that are handed to him are surely the work of the devil. Studded all over with sharp wooden protrusions these Spiked Indian Clubs require an inordinate amount of skill and precision to avoid serious injury to the user. But Holtum makes his contortions with them look easy. The audience momentarily pause from guzzling their bottles as he passes the fearsome studs close to his body, finishing with a flourish that has them drumming their feet.

During this last set piece a small cart has been wheeled into the ring filled with an assortment of different sized cannonballs. Setting aside the clubs Holtum picks up one of the cannon balls and calls a solid young man out from the audience. He drops the ball at the man's feet and asks him to lift it. The man leans forward, grinning, but turns red-faced when he struggles to lift it with two hands and the audience guffaws with laughter.

Dismissing the man Holtum deftly picks up the cannonball, throwing it high into the air. As he does so he leans forward, catching the ball with a dull thud on his back, absorbing the impact as though it were as fragile as an egg. The audience collectively winces. He then has a cannonball placed on the end of a rod balanced on his forehead and, before the audience have time to gather themselves, knocks the rod away, ducking his head forward to once again catch the ball between his shoulder blades. For the next ten minutes it seems there is little this extraordinary athlete cannot do with round, solid, lumps of metal. He balances them on his ankles, on his chin, in each hand and tosses them into the air with all the carefree joy of a boy playing with cricket balls. Either he has nerves of iron – or no nerves at all.

Even his jaw appears to be inhuman. At one point he places three cannonballs in a bag, takes the bag in his teeth and throws the whole thing backwards over his head. The audience cringe in unison as the bag slams into Holtum's back. Those who are sober find it exhausting to watch, others feel suddenly queasy.

Soon, however, it is time for the crowd to gain some ground of their own as the scene is set for the first challenge of the evening. A long wooden frame is brought into the ring and secured at one end to a roof column. Herr Holtum stretches out on the frame like a prisoner on the rack but face-down, with his head towards the column, his arms extended above his head, his hands gripping leather loops lashed around the top of the frame. Over his shoulders and round his waist is a well-padded harness, fitted with a tail to which is attached a large hook. On a signal from the ringmaster a local farmer and his boy enter the ring leading two large, blinkered plough horses whose traces are connected to the hook. The audience cheer loudly as Herr Holtum indicates he is ready, tensing his body as the horses are urged to move forward. The horses snort and stamp as they take the strain, their coats soon shining with sweat in the heat of the ring. In less than a minute Holtum's body appears stretched to breaking point as he fights to maintain his hold on the frame, the tension causing his arm muscles to bulge alarmingly. For four long minutes more, Harmston's circus is transformed into a raucous, bloodthirsty Roman arena, the audience shouting themselves hoarse in their desire to see the farmer triumph.

But despite a good deal of cajoling and slaps on the rump the horses fail to remove the man from the frame and the ringmaster has to fight to be heard as he announces the conclusion of the challenge. Tonight, Holtum gets to keep his money and the farmer will go away empty handed. The farmer shakes his head as he unhooks the traces and tips his hat to Herr Holtum who is being helped out of his harness. The baying of the crowd is replaced with loud applause and whistling as the farmer leads his exhausted animals from the ring.

After a short interlude in which most of the audience head for the bar the atmosphere changes yet again. Fraulein Anna returns to the ring, this time accompanied by a lively group of small dogs, all clinging to her heels, their tongues out, their eyes shining. Behind them come two young children walking steadily on two rolling globes, their fingertips just touching across the sawdust. What follows is a brave display of light-hearted tricks by mother, children and devoted canines but it is clear from the mood of the audience that they are impatient for something far more serious. The family leave the ring to a murmur of discontent.

Not that the crowd have long to wait. They are soon subdued into awed silence by the sight of a four-foot long cannon being drawn into the ring on a large-wheeled carriage pulled by two heavy horses. Another horse pulls a small wheeled conveyance filled with cannonballs. Herr Holtum guides the gun carriage into position and the horses are unhooked from the trail and led away.

The cannon's muzzle is positioned opposite a large wooden screen behind which the audience have been barred from sitting. The implications of the hollow, empty seats are not lost on the already-tense audience and they maintain their uneasy quiet as Herr Holtum places a sight in a hole on the top of the cannon and bends down to place his eye against it. With meticulous care he adjusts the angle of the cannon by the smallest degrees until he is satisfied and steps away, nodding to a man alongside him dressed in artillery uniform.

The man is carrying a shortened brass cartridge case filled with black powder and a small, fifteen pound cannonball. With the audience looking eagerly on he opens the rear of the cannon and pushes the case into the bore. He then turns a handle to close the breech and locks it in place with an ominous click. After cutting six inches of cannon fuse and placing it in the touch hole he announces that he is ready to fire.

With slow, elegant deliberation Holtum pulls on a pair of soot-blackened, thick leather gloves and covers his chest with a thick cuirass made of layers of paper. He then walks to the far side of the ring, turns to face the muzzle of the cannon and stands in a braced position, his gloved hands extended steadily in front of him. That he should display such calm while staring into the face of death is an unusually exciting and agitating experience and anyone in the audience who has a drop of rum left soon finishes it.

And now, it is the moment of truth. With a gesture to the audience to cover their ears, Holtum shouts 'Fire!', the gunner lights the fuse and for the next few excruciating seconds the auditorium is eerily silent apart from the hissing of the fuse as it burns slowly down. A thin line of smoke curls into the air. The audience hold their breath.

The silence is broken by an ear-shattering crack like thunder, accompanied by a flash and huge cloud of smoke as the ball shoots across the breadth of the arena. In the blink of an eye Herr Holtum is seen to pull his hands deftly backwards, catching the ball like a cricketer in the slips, staggering slightly as the force of its flight momentarily knocks him off balance. The ball is hot, red hot, and he can only maintain his hold on it for a second before dropping it to the sawdust where it lands with a heavy thud. The dense air in the circus is suddenly thick with the acrid, sulphurous smell of charcoal and salt petre, reminiscent of fireworks but, oh, so much more thrilling. It takes a moment for the audience to realise that Holtum is intact and unharmed. As the smoke clears they break into deafening cheers.

Twice more Herr Holtum repeats his extraordinary feat before the ringmaster announces the moment the audience have really been waiting for. It is time for the general public to step up to the plate. For a nervous minute or so there is a long, cavernous silence, before a smattering of slow hand claps, foot stomping and rude taunts persuade a handful of men to stand and make themselves known to Herr Holtum. Some are young, far too young, and to outbursts of laughter Holtum dismisses them with a gesture, telling them to try again when they have grown hair on their chests. But one of the willing contestants makes eye contact with Holtum and he calls him forward.

Thomas Boyde is well aware of the dangers involved in the challenge. He has seen plenty of cannon action during his time in the army and has recently spent many hours listening to Holtum talk about it in the Coffee Palace. But his military background makes him feel almost honour bound to 'pick up the glove' and he is keen to show that he is even more of a man to face up to it without a drink in him. Plus, Herr Holtum has made it known that since "the unfortunate occurrence" at Leeds the conditions for catching the ball and the distance the competitor stands from the gun are entirely different to what they were two years ago. The charge of powder is considerably less, consequently the distance traversed by the ball is less and whoever is competing has to hold a small flag in his left hand and catch the ball with the right hand only, thus keeping body and head out of the firing line. Easy, no?

Boyde enters the ring to loud cheers and strips off his coat and waistcoat. Holtum hands him a thick pair of gloves, ties the cuirass around his chest and instructs him to stand at a fixed point fifteen yards from the mouth of the cannon. Suddenly, despite all reassurances and his military training, Boyde can only stare at it in open fear and is sweating like a pig. In what seems like a far distant voice Herr Holtum is telling him he can have one attempt and one attempt only. He must heed Holtum's every word, he must not speak and on no account must he move. On the word 'Fire!' he is to catch the ball and a hundred pounds will be his. Holtum raises one eyebrow and smiles wickedly at the audience, who howl in anticipation.

As the gunner steps forward to light the fuse Thomas Boyde says a silent prayer and grits his teeth. Herr Holtum is watching him intently. The crowd have gone ominously quiet. And then in a flash and a thunderous roar the cannon fires its deadly missile.

Immediately after the performance John Holtum retreats to the outhouse where his cannon is to be kept overnight under lock and key. Once again it has served him well, his true and faithful servant. With a bucket of hot soapy water he carefully washes the cannon all over, flushing the barrel and cleaning the bore to remove all traces of black residue. After drying it thoroughly with a towel he whispers into its muzzle, and leaves it with a smile, checking the locks of the outhouse one last time as he looks around to ensure he's not being watched.

Meanwhile, outside the circus a small crowd has gathered in upper Church Street around a tall, well-built man who wears a blue ribbon pinned to his waistcoat. He's sweating and pale and his hands are shaking. Thomas Boyde may still have all his limbs but he is no richer than he was two hours ago. And he has never been so badly in need of a drink.

Addendum

In the year following his visit to the Isle of Man, John Holtum finally came up against someone who called his bluff. Amidst scenes of great excitement, an Irish shipbuilder named Charles Gleeson successfully caught the fired cannon ball and was duly paid the winner's jackpot, acquiring hero status among his colleagues.

In 1885, while performing in Newcastle, Holtum introduced a new military spectacle entitled 'The War in the Sudan' in which he played Sergeant Braveheart, the captured sergeant of a company of British soldiers. Tied up with rope, he was placed in front of a cannon and the order was given to 'fire!'. One evening, after the ball whizzed past his head, Holtum was released from his ropes but left the ring looking dazed, and when he re-appeared five minutes later, his head was bleeding and he held a blood-stained cloth in his hand. Ever the trooper, however, he quickly re-assured the audience that it was only a minor wound, asked the band to play 'God Save the Queen' and brought the performance to a close.

Within five years Holtum was being accompanied in the ring by his fifteen year old daughter Alvira, catching a cannonball with one hand and exercising with clubs.

John Holtum frequently travelled to America where he eventually settled in the late 1890s. In April 1898, at the age of fifty-two, he married his second wife, Catherine Gertson and changed his stage name to Captain Holtum. As a performer he maintained an international reputation and was even the basis for political cartoons in German newspapers, representing Bismarck catching the cannonballs of criticism and envy fired at him by enemies. He was still performing in 1906, appearing in Mexico forty years after his first appearance in that country. In spite of a 'chequered career', he was said to be in perfect health and looking forward to another European tour.

Holtum died in Oakland, California, in January 1912 aged sixty-six and is buried in the Mountain View Cemetery.

Chapter Twelve

THE CIRCUS FAMILY

1883 Sunday 17th June

What a fine day is in prospect! Eugene Cooke, manager of the large establishment now engaged at the circus building in Upper Church Street, has organised an excursion to the pleasure grounds at Glen Helen for his entire company and they could not be more delighted.

Eugene – known as Gene, his wife Helena, their seven young children and a lively handful of circus artistes are staying at Mrs Fleming's lodging house on Circular Road in Douglas and the chatter over breakfast has been all about the possibilities offered by Glen Helen. It's advertised as one of the largest and most popular recreational destinations on the island and Gene's eldest daughter Ida – twelve years old and a seasoned performer – is especially excited by the idea of croquet and flying high on the swings. Her younger siblings are looking forward to playing hide and seek in the park, and the two young clowns Thomas Green and Thomas Shufflebotham (better known in the ring as Toney Felix and Tom Yorick) are hopeful of a quiet spot of trout fishing in the river. The American vaulter Eggie Madigan is also up for some welcome diversions. He has all the energy of a wound-up spring and plans to enjoy some vigorous lawn games, while the circus band leader Captain Tucker, a jovial Irishman, is already looking ahead to a generous knife and fork tea, and has only nibbled a slice of toast at breakfast for fear of ruining his appetite.

Mrs Fleming's is only around the corner from Upper Church Street and by nine o'clock on this bright, clear June morning her spirited lodgers have gathered outside the front doors of the circus to meet with other company members and process en masse to the nearby railway station. As they walk others spill out from nearby lodgings and by the time they are assembled on the platform the colourful throng numbers more than a hundred people, all dressed in their Sunday best and apparently without a care in the world.

Gene Cooke has reserved all the compartments on the ten o'clock train and once his company have claimed their seats they turn and wave to the dozens of holidaymakers already milling about, waiting for the next service. At a signal from the guard the locomotive lets out a hiss of steam and pulls slowly out of the station in a black cloud of acrid, sooty smoke. Within minutes Douglas is behind them and the only sights are green hills that fade to a pale, distant purple; long gorse hedges that criss-cross the countryside like vivid yellow ribbons and flat meadows on either side of the track that swirl with tall, flowering crops. Every now and then the train passes through signposted stops but these are little more than tin huts sandwiched between small, thatched, whitewashed cottages where villagers, accustomed to the daily passage of thousands of holidaymakers, don't even look up as it thunders by.

Gene and his family have a compartment all to themselves and Ida spends most of her time with her face pressed against the window. This pleasant Manx countryside is a world away from the grimy towns of northern England that lie just across the water. Further down the carriage some of the more reckless passengers ignore the guard's warning and pull the windows all the way down so they can stick their heads out and soak up the sun. The very idea of time off without errands or chores to attend to is making them giddy.

One such passenger is Eggie Madigan. He rarely travels without his wife but she's still confined after giving birth so today he's been jammed into a compartment with Ada Isaacs the female jester, and the Eldred family of equestrians - Walter, his sisters Blonde and Jennie and younger brothers, ten year old Gilbert and four year old Frank. Like Eggie, the Eldreds are from pioneer stock, the offspring of a successful American circus proprietor who brought his family to England a number of years ago and established them as highly respected, daring, bare-backed riders – even young Frank, who's known in the ring as 'Baby Eldred, the smallest equestrian in the world!'

But it's Blonde who usually melts the hearts of the audience. Contrary to expectation she's actually a brunette, her given name referring not to her hair colour but to the name of the trans-Atlantic steamer on which she was born, and she's only a slip of a girl, petite and fine-boned with a tiny waist and elfin face - an appearance which belies her giant personality in the ring. Today, she's enjoying the chance to dispense with her restrictive riding habit in favour of a blue skirt with large bustle and a tailored satin jacket, puffed at the shoulders and gaily striped in white, blue and lemon. It's an outfit that anticipates a day of pure pleasure.

Ada Isaacs, the female jester, has also traded her somewhat masculine professional garb for something lighter and more frivolous, though her attempt at femininity sits awkwardly with her conversation. In the ring she is a vibrant purveyor of songs, jokes and dance, but in ordinary company her stories are often filled with drama and tragedy. Besides which, she assumes an American accent, to the irritation of her travelling companions who understand she's spent only a short time in the United States. However, they recognise a good self-publicist when they see one and generally swallow her tall tales with good humour.

In the adjacent compartment the conversation is considerably more vigorous. The two clowns Tom Yorick and Toney Felix have been joined by the company's youthful acrobats, 'Tom-Tom' Levon and Frank Van der Velde and a couple of other young men, and in the absence of female companions their constant stream of jokes and lewd observations have turned the air blue. But Tom Levon is especially thankful for the distracting chatter. Life has been hard lately - for him and for his family. His poor wife is in the asylum, he's struggled to find employment and pay his debts, and a few months ago one of his children died because he couldn't put enough food on the table. Today's outing makes him feel somewhat guilty but working for Mr Cooke has given him the chance to put things right and for the next few hours he can put his troubles to one side and enjoy some hearty male company.

Once the train reaches the small hamlet of St Johns the guard shouts for everyone to alight as it's necessary for the remaining two and a half miles to Glen Helen to be completed in horse-drawn conveyances. A dozen cabs are quickly filled and they are soon heading inland in a northerly direction, up a rough, winding road that leads into a river valley bordered by increasingly steep, rocky sides and thick vegetation. And they are not alone. A long line of carts, coaches and carriages packed with visitors already snakes ahead of the circus party as far as the eye can see.

Just as both horses and travellers are beginning to tire the imposing Glen Helen Hotel comes into view to the right of the road, alongside the grand entrance to the hundreds of acres of river valley that make up the glen itself. The carriages carrying the circus party squeeze into the busy car stands and the men alight first, catching the children who jump into their arms.

Entrance to the pleasure grounds is normally fourpence per person but Gene has made a prior arrangement with the manager and the circus party are quickly ushered through the gates where they are greeted by the sound of music and laughter. Following the noise, they navigate a neat pathway that meanders between immaculate lawns and flower beds until it opens out into a wide glade that makes the circus artistes catch their breath. It's as though they have been transported to the Swiss mountains; the scene before them is stunning. The far side of the valley is thick with a lush, dark green canopy of larch, sycamore, hazel, oak, ash and chestnut trees but it's the wooden cottage nestled into the base of the near hillside that immediately draws the eye. It's like something out of a fairy tale. Built to resemble an alpine chalet, the cottage is encircled by a wooden verandah and sits beneath a steeply sloping, four-sided roof that cocoons it like a snug hat. Dormer windows peep out of the roof as though anticipating heavy snow, and a variety of national flags ripple in the breeze to greet visitors from faraway lands. Blackboards hung at the cottage door advertise the activities included in the Glen's admission charge – croquet, lawn tennis, bowls, badminton and swings - and the company are quick to line up for racquets and mallets. Before they are allowed to disperse, however, Gene reminds them to all meet up again in half an hour to walk up river to the famous Rhenass waterfall.

The source of the music is soon revealed to be the Glen's brass band playing in the welcome shelter of a circular stand on the lawn below the cottage, while the laughter is generated by a group of young children cavorting in the spray from an ornate two-tiered, cast iron fountain decorated at the base with four lifelike white swans. Almost every inch of grass around the fountain is occupied by families picnicking on sandwiches, cake and lemonade in the shade of giant fir trees.

Beyond the picnic spot the grounds slope down to a wooden bridge that leads to a recreation area taken up with ball games and gaily painted swings. Ida has already claimed her seat and is being pushed skyward by Walter Eldred. Eggie Madigan is leaping around the badminton court like a man possessed.

Helena, meanwhile, settles herself and her younger children on a large rug on the lawn. She's a handsome woman of thirty-six years, with lustrous, dark, auburn-tinted hair; large, deep-set green eyes and a permanent tilt to her mouth that hints she has just been told something amusing. The company adore her. She is their mother hen, an accomplished equestrian who performs in the ring yet still manages to find the time for her own family and her fellow professionals. Today she's wearing her finest outfit, a plum silk and straw bonnet finished with black feathers, a fashionable dress of fitted magenta silk trimmed with black lace, soft kid gloves, ornate drop earrings and her customary gold locket on a long chain. She has put up her parasol and her youngest children – three year old Alfred and two year old Edgar – curl up beneath it. The older children – ten year old Cissie, Cyril nine, Victoria six and Eva five, are more intent on a game of tag. They have boundless energy and although at present only Ida has followed her parents into the ring it is taken as read that the others will not be far behind.

Soon Helena is joined by her husband who sprawls on the rug and allows himself to be jumped on by the youngest of his brood. Gene is very good looking, in a slightly rumpled, louche sort of way. He has dark, almond-shaped eyes and a neat beard and moustache, but his short, dark curly hair is forever wild and unruly and his flattened, crooked nose bears all the hallmarks of youthful exuberance. These days his stints in the ring are centred around horsemanship but in his younger days he was better known as the daring trapeze artist 'Eugene the Marvellous', a career that took him to dizzy heights in every sense and brought him fame and a fair amount of fortune. However, once his family began to grow he felt the need for something more down to earth and when his cousins John and Harry offered him a stake in their Cooke Brothers Circus 'Eugene the Marvellous' became 'Eugene the Manager'.

It may not have quite the same ring about it but management has certainly suited him. He is good with people and prefers to concentrate on the workings of his company rather than his own ambitions. In fact, today he would prefer not to think about business at all as, for the next few hours, he and his family have much more pleasant matters to attend to. The whole company will be sitting down to lunch at half past two and before then they are to make their way up the glen to see the waterfall, three quarters of a mile upstream.

While Helena and the two youngest children stay behind, Gene takes Ida and her siblings onto the path that follows the left hand side of the river and they are soon joined by the rest of the company. The path gains height quickly and before long there is a drop of about thirty feet to the swirling water below. None of the party has any fear of heights, even the youngest members, and they all stand close to the edge to peer into the cutting. Beneath them the river appears black and oily in the shade of the ravine and the party can hear the distant voices of Toney Felix and Tom Yorick, who have borrowed fishing rods and nets to try and catch some of the trout the glen is known for.

Across the river the valley is thickly wooded and dense with dappled light and birdsong but this side has a much more open feeling, the trees being very sparse after a recent fire, and the exposed bank is studded with large rocks. On drawing away from the edge of the river some of the young acrobats turn their attention to the embankment, deftly scaling the rocks like mountain goats and leaping expertly down onto the path without even a stumble.

As the path climbs they pass quaint little summerhouses and rustic wooden seats and soon come to a high wooden bridge that spans the river, supported by two stone columns. Frank Van der Velde is the first to take advantage of the bridge's construction. In the circus ring his specialty is the 'Ladder of Life' and, with a dexterous leap, he's soon standing confidently on the top wooden rails of the bridge, from where he walks to the middle and pauses for a minute to take in his spectacular, natural surroundings. To applause and whistles from his colleagues - and astonished holidaymakers who have stopped to stand and stare - Frank slowly leans forward, places his head on the top rail, grips with his hands and lifts his legs. Gene raises his eyebrows but doesn't attempt to stop him. In the ring this fearless young man would also be drinking from a glass of water and smoking a cigar while inverted upside down at the top of a ladder. Gene shakes his head and urges the party to move on. Behind them Frank returns to a standing position on the rail tops, walks swiftly along to the end and somersaults neatly onto the path.

Ida is enjoying this relaxed time with her father and links her arm through his as they progress towards the waterfall. As they walk, he reminds her of her proud circus heritage. Nowadays she has relatives all over the world, nearly all of them employed in the circus, but it all began way back in the last century with her great, great grandfather Thomas Cooke - a strongman from the south of England – who set up his own travelling circus at a time when the concept of circus was only new. His son, Thomas Taplin Cooke, then followed him into the business and became one of the first circus proprietors to ship an entire establishment – including forty members of the Cooke family - across the Atlantic to America. For a while they did well, but then devastating fires took them to the brink of bankruptcy and Thomas returned to Britain and turned his attention to Scotland and the north of England where the name Cooke soon became one of the most respected in the business.

Now, generations later, Gene is unashamedly proud of his own young daughter. Practically raised on horseback she is already winning an army of admirers, performing with her ponies Alice and Beeswing. Last night they were recalled twice by the audience in Douglas and Gene has high hopes for her future.

As the rest of the company make their way further up the glen the rocky sides of the valley begin to narrow and darken, dripping with water that seeps through thick layers of moss and lichen. Here the vegetation is dotted with ferns and sunlight filters through the trees in long white ribbons. But there is still plenty of opportunity for improvised fun. At one point a fallen tree is perched precariously over the river, its giant roots exposed to the air like a tattered wig. The trunk is instantly transformed into an impromptu tightrope. Down below, where the river surges between giant boulders, groups of artistes squeeze on top of the flat granite slabs, allowing jester Ada Isaacs to hold court in her curious drawl with witty songs and ribald stories. All around them the river echoes their laughter as it gushes over dark green slimy rocks and swirls through deep pools and eddies.

Attaining the path once again, the party continues north until the track begins to level off and the valley opens out to low-growing, native woodland, dense with blossoming rowan and hawthorn. Sunlight sparkles on lumps of quartz sticking out of the ground and the air is beautiful here, soft, fresh and gently fragrant. The circus artistes, more used to the cloying smells of sawdust, dung, chalk and body odour, feel wonderfully invigorated.

As they walk their voices are gradually drowned out by a deep rumble that forces them to shout to make themselves heard. Then, suddenly, with roaring in their ears, the party turn into a sunny glade where they are faced by a tall, jagged cliff that dramatically marks the convergence of two rivers. On the southern side of the glade the water flows quietly around the base of the cliff whereas on the northern side it flows through the very rock itself, forcing its way out through a high, narrow gorge and creating a powerful cascade of white water - the famous Rhenass Falls - which thunders dozens of feet into a large, shallow pool below.

For a moment the circus performers are stopped in their tracks. And then, as one body, they race over the wooden bridge that crosses the point where the two rivers meet and hurriedly remove their boots and stockings. The water of the pool is icy and tinged brown with peat from the upland hills but they still hoot with pleasure as they paddle in its foam-flecked shallows.

Cooled and refreshed they set their sights on further exploration. Signs indicate access to a bridge built thirty feet above the point where the water surges out of the gorge and Eggie Madigan energetically leads the way. The path takes them up a steep incline that winds behind the cliff and, as they climb, a number of other picturesque waterfalls and cascades are revealed. Having reached the main bridge they pile into its centre and gaze down on the valley laid out before them. From here they can see the Swiss cottage and pleasure grounds in the far distance and, looking even further to the Island's west coast, a strip of pale blue where the sea joins the sky. Tiny Blonde Eldred pushes her way to the front of the bridge and calls out a greeting, her small voice bouncing off the hillside. Soon her colleagues all join in and visitors walking in the Glen wonder at the sound that is resonating through the trees.

The walk back to the pleasure ground is completed in half the time. The party are hungry now and mindful of Gene Cooke's earlier instructions - be respectable of the glen and its patrons, try not to break any limbs, and don't be late for luncheon!

Captain Tucker is already seated by the time they return, a large white napkin covering his shirt. At half past two every Sunday during the season the Glen Helen Hotel lays on a five course table d'hote spread and the Captain does not want to miss a single crumb. The rest of the company fill the remaining tables and soon a procession of food is placed in front of them, the like of which many of them have never even seen before let alone tasted. Russian salad, devilled eggs, fillets of mackerel, celery soup, fancy rolls, chicken and ham pie, new potatoes, broad beans and, to finish – for those still with an appetite – pound cake, strawberry jelly, vanilla cream and the famed Glen Helen cheesecakes.

At the end of the meal Eggie Madigan stands and asks his colleagues to raise a glass to their generous hosts, the Cooke family. On the top table Gene and Helena acknowledge the gesture with wide smiles and the children break into a frenzy of clapping. It certainly has been a most enjoyable day. No bones were broken, the performers have roses in their cheeks and the bonds of the circus family have been nurtured and strengthened. The rest of the season should play out well.

Addendum

Later in June Ida made her debut in the character of 'The Wee Scotch Lassie' and completely won the house with a performance on her bare-backed pony. Her father Eugene was said to look very proud of his little daughter and reporters predicted that she would be a star in her profession.

At the end of the season the circus band leader Mr Tucker led a public presentation to Helena Cooke of a gold bracelet, set with three rubies and two diamonds, bought from local jeweller Mr Little. The bracelet was accompanied by an address, printed on satin. Mr Tucker said the bracelet was a slight token of the respect in which Mrs Cooke was held by the entire company.

In 1884 the Madigan family embarked for India on board the P&O steamer Bokhara, for an engagement with The Great World Circus Company. The following spring Lizzie Madigan gave birth to a son in Bombay but only two days later she and Eggie lost their infant daughter Madeline.

In 1884 Ada Isaacs, the female jester, was in court to hear her husband, the clown James Fagin, charged with bigamy. The court alleged that while married to Ada he also married a female circus performer employed by Hengler's. Fagin denied ever being married to Ada.

Tony Felix later discovered the perils of being a stilt walker. In 1885 whilst walking on stilts through Wigan in a circus procession he was knocked over by children running between his stilts, breaking his left arm and two fingers.

In the summer of 1888 Ida Cooke, then seventeen years old, created newspaper headlines when she tried to elope with a young American, the cousin of the late American Ambassador in London. Walter Dodge fell for Ida when she rode in the circus at Keswick and persuaded her to run away with him. The pair boarded a train for Glasgow but were intercepted by the police who'd been alerted by her father. Eugene Cooke escorted his daughter back to Keswick but Walter Dodge, undeterred, telegraphed his parents in New York asking for their consent to his marriage with Miss Cooke by special licence. A week later the young couple eloped again and this time they were successfully married in Edinburgh, a move that deeply affected Ida's father. They soon left England for America where they set up home and had three children. The marriage was not to last, however, and Ida married again in 1902, becoming Mrs Robinson, and eventually passed away in California at the age of one hundred.

Eggie Madigan died at the age of thirty four in 1892 after a distinguished career as principal vaulter with Hengler's, Boswell's, Cooke's and Myers' Circuses and a reputation throughout Europe and India. His death was said to be peaceful but it was widely believed that the many accidents he experienced during his career contributed to his death.

That same year Peppino George Harmston married Blonde Eldred in Yokohama, Japan.

Helena Cooke died in 1890 and three years later her husband Eugene married Emily Adams, twenty-three years his junior.

Chapter Thirteen

THE LITTLE CHILDREN

1885 Thursday 9th July

A young girl, dressed in a straw hat and wooden clogs, fidgets before her increasingly impatient mother. The girl is due at the new circus on Upper Church Street later this morning and she's restless and sick with nerves. Her home in Fairy Ground – a dark, narrow lane off the North Quay, crammed with tall, timeworn buildings – has little in the way of natural light and it's hard to judge whether her outfit will pass muster. Her hand-me-down dress, originally bright green, is now an indeterminate sludge colour from years of wear and washing, and her once-white pinafore is yellowed and blotched with stubborn stains. The day is already warm and her woollen drawers are making her itchy. Just before she leaves home her mother pins a clean, pressed handkerchief to her pinafore and the crisp cotton contrasts sharply with her dreary clothing.

Visitors to Douglas always assume – quite reasonably – that Fairy Ground must be a place where fairies live. But the girl knows otherwise. Her mother says the name simply recalls the fair that used to be held here in the old days. Which seems more likely to the girl for why would fairies want to live here? The ancient beach cobbles in the lane are covered by a thick layer of silt and animal waste which turns to muddy slop in the winter and brown dust in the summer. The tall houses are dank and oppressive and the air is always tainted by earthy smells of beer, unwashed bodies, fish guts and overflowing privvies, made worse on hot summer days by the acrid black smoke from steam ships that muffles the old town like a blanket. Woe betide any well-heeled visitor that unwittingly strays into Fairy Ground.

The three-storey house in which the girl and her large family occupy two top-floor rooms is sandwiched between another overcrowded house and a rowdy inn. In this part of old Douglas the dwellings, shops and taverns are stacked up against one another like a pack of badly shuffled cards, their higgledy-piggledy roof lines hiding a maze of filthy cobbled streets that twist and bend at crooked angles and lead blindly into tapered alleyways and secret courtyards.

The appearance of the house is drab in the extreme. The narrow frontage is finished with patchy, grey cement streaked with black soot and green algae, the windows are rimed with dirt and salt, and a section of the warped roof hangs perilously over the street below. Inside, the damp, dingy rooms are linked by a dark, confined stairwell and beneath the gloomy centre passage on the ground floor, a set of stone steps leads down to a disused cellar that fills with sea water when the tide comes in. On stormy nights the tenants in the lower rooms can hear the water lapping against the steps and the scuttling of the 'long tails' that swim in with the tide.

But it's not all bleak. At the back of the house the passage opens out into a small yard with a stunted apple tree in one corner, and a shared privy and stone pig shed in the other. During the summer, when there's plenty of herring and mackerel, the fish is brought into the yard in a big barrel and divided up between the neighbours. There may not be any fairies here but there are good people.

Once the girl is ready to leave for the circus she clatters down the stairs and out onto the gloomy lane, turning swiftly in the direction of the harbour. The uneven surface makes walking hard on her ankles and her clogs rub as she quickens her pace, flattening herself against a doorway every now and then to let carts pass carrying sacks of coke or kegs of beer. As she emerges into bright sunshine on the quay she is quickly swallowed up in a throng of people going about their business or making purchases from the traders dotted along the quayside. A large man in a leather apron hands out paper cones filled with oysters sprinkled with salt, pepper and vinegar; fish merchants tout their 'fresh herrin' to crowds of women who pile the slippery 'silver darlings' into crocks and dishes, and flower sellers wrapped in colourful shawls sit patiently in the sun behind bright bunches of dahlias, heather and cornflowers.

The girl's favourite vendor is the cheap-jack in a checked suit who stands on the corner peddling tins full of toffee, his voice competing with paper boys calling out the day's headlines. And the toffee seller certainly knows his audience. The crowd is full of children. A group of small boys perch on the edge of the pavement outside the coffee house, tossing marbles in the dust. Half a dozen girls, hair flying, dodge between horses and pedestrians, chasing an iron hoop that jangles on the cobbles, and, in the background, high reedy voices can be heard singing to the tunes of a barrel organ being turned on a wheeled cart.

Regretfully, the girl has no time to linger. From the quay she turns up Market Hill then into Duke Street, past dozens of small shops, before coming out onto Victoria Street from where she hurries up the hill to the circus.

By the time she reaches the circus the girl's nose is running. She wipes it on a sleeve that is ragged at the edges, reluctant to use her handkerchief before she is seen by the circus business manager. She needs to impress him and, aside from her straw hat, the clean handkerchief is the only thing about her that is smart and decent. As she waits she looks down at her feet, blistered now from her long walk. Her clogs are borrowed and too big and they have left red welts on her bare skin.

Dozens of other children have already made their approach to Boswell's Circus manager, Mr Johnson, and a few have been told to come back for rehearsal tomorrow but he is being very particular. Children who cannot walk straight or appear before him without shoes and hats are turned away. The juvenile performers will be paid three and sixpence a week and it's money Mr Boswell is loath to squander on unsuitable candidates.

Eventually the girl is ushered in front of Mr Johnson. He's in his late twenties but has an attitude of brisk efficiency that makes him seem much older. He takes her hands and turns them over to inspect the palms then twists her round, looking her up and down, before asking her to walk a few paces, turn on the spot and stand still when instructed. Finally, he nods and tells her she will do but when she returns tomorrow she's to come with clean hands, face and feet, and her hair, if unwashed, must be tied back with a ribbon. And she **must** attend the circus every day thereafter or she won't get her money.

As the girl makes to leave a young boy enters the office. He's probably only four years old, in badly-patched trousers and a threadbare, button-less jacket. He has no cap to cover his grimy shaven scalp and his naked feet are black with ingrained dirt. Arthur Johnson shakes his head and sends him away. 'Cinderella' may be based on a tale of rags to riches but his little pantomime actors do not have to be quite so grounded in reality.

Boswell's have been entertaining good houses in Douglas since the start of July in the circus building originally built five years ago by Charlie Keith but, with the holiday season in full swing and thousands of parents seeking out wholesome family entertainment, it will soon be time for a change of programme. 'Cinderella' is a tried and trusted favourite –Keith's company performed it in this very same building - and if Boswell's can recruit enough youngsters from the local populace it should give them an edge over the competition. And better still, according to Arthur Johnson, it will temporarily reduce their wage bill.

The advert for 'one hundred pretty little children' to audition for the pantomime was placed only days ago but it has drawn four times that number, with scores of children streaming out of their dwellings like hungry mice, pushing, shoving and chattering in high, exuberant voices in their rush to be seen by Mr Johnson. And they have come from all corners of town. From the smart new houses at the top of the hill and terraced lodgings that line the bay, to the crowded courts, squalid cottages and dark, dank back alleys that squat behind the harbour. Some of the children are little more than toddlers, tightly gripping the hands of their older siblings who themselves are only just aged in double figures. A few are accompanied by their parents, keen to see what the fuss is about and ensure their offspring are not overlooked, but the majority are left to their own devices, as they are on every other day.

Naturally, all the children are excited by the advertisement's promise of bright lights and glamour. Earning a few shillings for taking part in a 'fairy spectacle' is a good deal more appealing than guarding newly-washed sheets on the riverbank or delivering high-smelling meat for the local butcher. But, for most, the real draw is the prospect of the hot meat pie or dozen oysters their wages will secure.

What's more, they don't even have to learn any words! The main action of the pantomime will be performed in dumb-show, and the successful Douglas candidates will play dancers and guests in the ballroom scene. Only the main characters will be required to speak and these parts have already been allocated to the offspring of the circus folk. Arthur Johnson's son, Arthur Frederick, will play the part of Prince Charming and Cinderella will be played by the ringmaster's young daughter Priscilla Roberts. Her father Rudolph is charged with directing the production, as he has done for a few seasons now, and her mother will organise the costumes.

As Arthur Johnson concludes his auditions he assures the last nervous hopefuls that, as long as they obey the ringmaster's instructions and do as they're told, their pantomime debut should bring the house down.

On the first morning of rehearsal the successful little actors are initially divided up into groups under the charge of various performers. Some are put into the care of Mr Boswell's sisters, two pretty equestrians. Others, including the girl from Fairy Ground, are given to the charge of the jester, who also plays the part of the Fairy Godmother in the pantomime. On introduction he presents a forbidding sight, only half dressed in rubber cap, pantaloons, vest and braces, his face chalked and a grubby towel slung over his shoulder, but he seems jolly enough and quickly has the youngsters laughing with silly rhymes and playful pinching.

The morning still, however, proves undeniably challenging. The children are clearly fascinated by their new surroundings and easily distracted, not least by the fact that most of the artistes – men and women - seem to go about in various states of undress. And they use curious words which the children struggle to understand. Nor does it help matters that they have to wait for a young 'bender' to finish rehearsing before they can file into the ring. To keep them focussed and prevent any mischief Mr Roberts has them fill the seats on the edge of the circle instead of waiting in the Green Room. Here, he thinks, they will be able to see first-hand just how much hard work and concentration is required by even the youngest of performers.

The 'bender' is the boy contortionist known as Pheaton, apprenticed to the equilibrist – or balancer - Mr Henry Foden. In the cold, half-light of the vast empty arena, his face obscured by shadow, the tiny boy appears like one of the 'little people' – small, weightless and unworldly. The children watch enthralled as he twists his seemingly boneless, elasticized body into incredible shapes, while his master walks around him all the while, clicking his fingers and tapping him with a long cane.

The boy begins by leaning over backwards until his hands are flat on the floor, his body curved like a crab, his eyes heavenward, then slowly lifts his feet up until his body is balanced entirely on his hands. He then 'walks' a few paces on his hands before coming gracefully out of the handstand and, in one fluid movement, stands upright and, raises his foot, grasping his ankle in one hand and extending his leg in a straight line above his head. Occasionally Mr Foden steps in to support him with his hands, but his tutoring seems to consist largely of clicking, tapping and constant urging to stretch harder, hold his breath longer and 'smile, smile, smile!'

After fifteen minutes of strenuous contortion Mr Foden instructs the boy to lie face down on a mat on the floor, raise his head and stretch his arms backwards to grab his ankles. To the amazement of the watching children, and with some help from his master, the boy then pulls his legs down over his shoulders so that his feet are either side of his head, creating an almost perfect circle with his flexible torso. Some of the girls, disturbed by such an unnatural sight, gag and cover their eyes, moaning, until warned by the ringmaster to control themselves.

In the ring the little boy slowly unknots himself and shakes his limbs, keeping his eyes averted as he rubs his neck. It's only as he leaves the ring, passing close by the children, that they catch a clear glimpse of his face, the dark circles beneath his eyes creating black saucers against his pallid skin.

Mr Roberts is impatient to get on but does his best not to show it. His own daughter and the other children who travel with Boswell's are well used to the routine of circus life but he perceived early on that this lot of ragamuffins would take some moulding - and he can only pray that eagerness to earn a few shillings and wear pretty costumes will keep them focussed.

Indeed, by the time Mr Roberts is ready to dismiss them, the children are considerably more at ease in their strange new surroundings. Even after being told to return home a small group of boys dawdle at the entrance to the yard while the horses are brought up from the stables. One of the grooms tosses the boys some apples and there's a minor tussle as they scramble over one another to retrieve the fruit from the straw-covered cobbles. But they feel shy of lingering too long. Everyone here clearly has a job to do and work is soon found for idle hands. All around them circus children scurry about their business, crossing the yard with giant dogs twice their size or staggering beneath great armfuls of costumes and coils of rope. Turning to leave, the boys nearly knock over a young lad balancing a bucket on his head while simultaneously spinning a hoop on his ankle and feeding a small monkey perched on his shoulder. This may be a world built on thrills and fantasy but there is clearly little time for day dreaming.

Wednesday 12th August

Douglas is bursting at the seams. The newspapers talk of eighteen thousand holidaymakers lodging in the town, and that's in addition to the thousands of locals attempting to carry on their usual business. Tickets for the pantomime have been selling well since it opened last Monday, and tonight a Grand Fashionable Night is being held under the patronage and presence of the visitors of the Grand and Royal Hotels. The children have been rehearsing doggedly for weeks and Mr Roberts is fairly pleased with the way they have picked things up. Naturally, most of them have never done anything like this before and for the first few days they had to be reined in like circus horses, with a sharp word or two if they lost concentration and started fooling around. A few have fallen by the wayside, unable to comprehend instructions no matter how oft repeated, and one or two have been dismissed for thieving, but on the whole they've been quick to learn and certainly have more colour in their cheeks than the sallow, lethargic creatures he's worked with in cities across the water.

The pantomime is being performed every evening during the week, and three afternoons, and the girl from Fairy Ground has already made the journey once today for the matinee. When she arrives back at the door of the circus for tonight's Grand Fashionable performance she finds chaos in Upper Church Street. Dozens of children are milling about, waiting for Mr Johnson to let them in. When the doors open they push through, eager to get into their fine costumes and paint their faces. While they are getting ready Mr Boswell – J.C as he is known – comes to the dressing room to say hello and they greet him with awed silence. He travels with his five young children – four years and under – and it's known they were born with circus in their veins. J.C's grandfather was a big circus man; he himself is renowned for his marvellous way with horses and stylish riding, and his wife Louisa was born into a well-known circus family. Tonight the oldest of his children will show their colours with small roles in the pantomime.

Boswell's do occasionally come up against criticism for their use of juveniles but J.C always quotes the example of his own children – they're always with their parents, they all work together, eat together, travel together. Yes, discipline is necessary for all children in the circus but that's because they're surrounded by adults who have a tough job to do and there's little scope for fooling around. And any discipline has to be measured. You cannot horsewhip a smile onto a child's face. An ill-treated child rarely makes a good performer and some circus people say you're more likely to see cruelty in the homes of well-to-do Englishmen raising their children to be ornaments in society!

The evening begins with a flourish from the band. The guests from the Grand and Royal hotels are in the most expensive seats with a clear view of the ring and, backstage, the pantomime children are hushed by the Jester as they await their turn.

'Cinderella' is timed for the middle of the programme and beforehand the audience is treated to the usual array of circus regulars – equestrians, clowns and jugglers. There's also a troupe of boy acrobats led by a man who calls himself the Professor. Outside the ring the Douglas children have heard the boys address him as 'Father' but no-one is sure of the truth of this. Every day they've watched the boys practising their moves and gawped at some of the hazardous stunts expected of them. Tonight, the smallest lad – about four years old - comes on dressed as a clown, tumbling like someone twice his age. The audience go mad for him, throwing oranges and sixpences which he scoops up into a little velvet pouch, hopping and bouncing around the ring on short, skinny legs. It's said that he made his debut as Tom Thumb when he'd only just learnt to walk and has since performed all sorts of business, including being 'baked' in a giant pie for the clown's dinner.

There is also, of course, a star turn by the young performer Pheaton. The children have gradually got to know him - although still only as Pheaton as he seems unsure of his real name, having been with Master Foden for as long as he can remember. Master Foden pays for his board and lodging, his clothes, his food, his training, and learning his letters. In return the boy says he's obliged to stay with him for a number of years, practising every day and producing a consistent performance to guarantee their wages. The children are agog but he says a generation ago boys were regularly apprenticed to the contortionist's trade, as if it were blacksmithing or carpentry. Families who find themselves on the skids will often offer their children up to the circus to relieve them of a burden. One lad he's heard of was taken by a trainer who gave his drunken mother two or three pounds a week for the care of him. But then the boy was given an education and a craft and now earns fifteen pounds a week!

The Douglas children have also listened wide-eyed as Pheaton described his early training. The very first thing he had to learn, at the age of six, was how to hold his breath, for certain moves can only be maintained without breathing. He then had to make his limbs stretch like they had never stretched before. Because he has to make his body extra-long or as small as a ball he has to exercise every day, lengthening his muscles and tendons with repetitive movements, dumb bells and work on the rings. The hardest manoeuvre to grasp was 'the splits' which is both uncomfortable and painful until it's properly mastered. Although he's never experienced it himself, he has heard of some boys having grown men sit on their shoulders to weigh them down – a nugget of wisdom which made the children shudder.

Tonight, the first part of the act performed by Pheaton and Master Foden is a polished version of the moves the children witnessed in early rehearsals, but the second part is a revelation.

Master Foden lies down on a sloped wooden board with his head at the lower end and raises his legs in the air, urging the boy to lean backwards and take his hands so that he can pull him up over the soles of his feet. Pheaton then curls up his limbs until he resembles a tight ball and, as the band strikes up a gay tune, the older man begins to move his feet, tossing the boy up into the air, going faster and faster until, after a minute or two, the boy is spinning like a Catherine Wheel. The audience go wild, filling the amphitheatre with loud whistles, hollering and thunderous clapping which only increases as Master Foden slows his pace, allowing Pheaton to jump down to the sawdust and take a bow.

It is an electrifying piece of human theatre that reeks of danger. Fortunately, tonight, in the presence of the respectable visitors, it has come off without incident. But even if it hadn't the Master says there's always the option of a name-change. A new name in a new town and the audience will be none the wiser.

Mr Roberts now enters the ring looking magnificent in a black swallow-tailed coat with red lapels, black trousers striped with gold, polished black shoes, a white shirt and bow tie, white gloves and black top hat. His hair shines with oil, his moustache is waxed to fine points and his cheeks glow with rouge. The children, more used to seeing him in a crumpled brown suit, hardly recognise him.

'Ladies and gentlemen,' he booms 'distinguished guests, prepare yourselves for a magical re-telling of one of the world's most popular tales. A moral fable of unjust oppression and triumphant reward. An expression of the power of goodness and humility over cruelty and wickedness. A gorgeous tableau that will warm the soul and soften even the hardest heart. Ladies and gentlemen, please, make yourselves comfortable for Boswell's Circus production of Cinderella, the 'Tale of the Little Glass Slipper', starring a cast of young starlets and children of the town of Douglas!'

The clowns have been distracting the audience while the scene is set for the pantomime, and when the band strikes up once more the light falls on a vision more usually seen in the theatre. The ring has been transformed with furniture and props to resemble a large country house kitchen and the action opens with the entrance of Cinderella herself - a dainty little girl with long blonde ringlets, dressed in a long, tatty cloak, who bows to the boxes, pit and gallery before taking her place by a washtub where she pretends to wash linen. After a few minutes two older girls, in fine gowns and thick face paint, enter the ring and berate their scruffy little servant, scolding her and making fun of her appearance. A loud murmur of sympathy emanates from the audience but their attention is soon diverted by an old crone, complete with outrageous false nose and dishevelled wig, who appears on the other side of the ring. The crone, in a disarmingly deep voice, asks for food and water but is driven away by the step-sisters who insist on Cinderella helping them instead, to dress for a ball.

It's only once the sisters have left the house that the action in the arena bursts into life. In a flash of light and smoke, the actor playing the crone reappears, this time wearing a flimsy white dress, ornamented with a blonde wig and fairy wand, announcing that 'she' is really Cinderella's Fairy Godmother and can grant her wish to go to the ball. The appearance of what is patently a man dressed as a woman initially induces loud sniggers from the audience but their mirth is quickly doused by the miraculous transformation – aided by more blasts of smoke – of a paper pumpkin into a small four-wheeled open carriage, complete with ornately painted and gilded wheels, drawn by four piebald circus ponies covered in ornate red cloths. At a flourish of the Godmother's wand Cinderella divests her long cloak to reveal a glittering ball gown trimmed with spangles and lace, and, on her feet, a pair of opaque satin slippers. With a warning that she must return home by midnight Cinderella hops into the little carriage and is driven from the ring.

The audience are transfixed. This is entertainment of a very different kind to that which they expect at the circus and the circular vista gives it a whole new dimension.

Behind the scenes, waiting in the corridor, the children of Douglas are shaking with nerves and excitement. The next scene takes place in the Grand Ballroom and their moment is about to come.

When Mr Roberts finally gives them the signal to enter the ring they experience a dazzling explosion of sights and sounds that, even after a week of performance, still threaten to overwhelm them. Boswell's Circus, home to clowns and acrobats, is now something akin to a royal palace. The sawdust in the ring has been overlaid with a large circle of gaily patterned carpet, on one side of which is a miniature minstrel's gallery, on the other a realistic lordly entrance hall hung with heavy drapes and between them a large gilded throne. Any gaps around the edges of the ring are filled with velvet-covered couches and chaise longues, and every inch of the ring wall has been lavishly decorated with vases of flowers and coloured ribbons. Presiding over everything is the ominous totem of a large grandfather clock which stands ready to beat out its twelve deadly strikes, and the whole scene is softly lit by dozens of candelabra.

The children of Douglas, their own dull clothes exchanged for sparkling gauze, coloured spangles, deep velvets and gold buttons, marshal into the ring carrying golden wands, banners and wreaths of roses. Many of them are costumed in the guise of familiar popular figures – here is Mary Queen of Scots on the arm of Napoleon, Mother Hubbard accompanies the gracious Shah of Persia and Mr Gladstone is partnered with Britannia. One young boy plays the old-English gentleman John Bull with particular gusto, drawing laughter from the crowd with his penchant for snuff.

What a treat this is. What a strange and wonderful experience. For audience and actors alike. Over the next half hour the children shut their minds to daily chores and cramped, cheerless homes and give themselves up to a world that is truly extraordinary. Even the dark stories they have seen and heard back stage are momentarily put to one side as they immerse themselves in a kaleidoscope of colour and light, skipping through the quadrille that has been drilled into them over the past two weeks, soaking up the heady atmosphere. The youngest ones, and those less adept at performance, simply walk in time to the music and sit ringside between movements, though some are so small they can scarcely climb up onto the couches.

And then, suddenly, the spell is broken by a burst of spontaneous applause from the audience as the ethereal figure of Cinderella appears in the centre of this vibrant melee, dancing a minuet with a handsome, boyish Prince – the young son of Mr Johnson - regal in tights, hose, and buckled shoes, a short cloak, a hat with a large feather in it, and, glued to his baby-faced chin, a short, pointed beard. The scene is mawkish and romantic and the audience lap up every minute until the clock ominously begins to strike midnight, the dancing is brought to an abrupt halt and Cinderella flees from the ballroom.

The next scenes see the love story unfold in the traditional manner. A second ball is staged in which the little kitchen maid disastrously forgets the time and leaves behind one of her slippers. The Prince scours the country for its owner and, in the happy ending that generations already know but never fail to enjoy, when Cinderalla produces the matching slipper the audience cheer with delight and the more sentimental amongst them, children and adults alike, shed a few tears. In true pantomime style the action draws to a conclusion with the Prince conveying his betrothed to the church to be married, as the circus band launch into their own unique version of the wedding march.

As the audience show their appreciation Rudolph Roberts and J.C Boswell peer through a gap in the ring curtain, keen to see the reaction of the specially invited hotel guests. But they appear to be as enthusiastic as everyone else, animated, clapping energetically and grinning from ear to ear. The children of Douglas have earned their reward.

The rest of the evening proceeds in the normal manner. J.C's sisters perform their magic on horseback, acrobats twirl and tumble to rounds of enthusiastic applause and the clowns provoke great ripples of laughter with their funny antics. But it's the golden splendour of the fairy spectacle which is the late-night talk of the drawing rooms at the Royal and George Hotels.

As the guests relax in their wing chairs to critique the performance, the girl from Fairy Ground is lining up in front of Mr Johnson to receive her well-earned sixpence. Wrapping the money carefully in her still clean handkerchief she places it in her pinafore pocket and sets out for home, her head spinning and her senses teeming. Halfway home in the now familiar streets behind the harbour, she removes her clogs and skips, barefoot, through the darkness.

Addendum

On a Friday evening in September large numbers of people flocked onto the Red Pier to witness Boswell's ringmaster Rudoph Roberts attempt to cross the harbour in a washing tub drawn by four live geese. As he took his seat in the frail craft Mr Roberts was cheered on by hundreds of spectators. He only had two small paddles, one of which broke, but he kept going and landed at the harbour just before seven o'clock.

By 1888 newspaper columnists were becoming openly critical of the training of very young children for acrobatic performances, describing it as barbarous and inhuman, with an unhealthy reliance on the whip, cane, slipper or boot. On newspaper called such apprenticeships business transactions in which heartless parents bartered their offspring to a childhood of misery, thereby escaping the cost of raising them. They called for public debate on the matter and wider awareness of the suffering of children in the industry, especially infant contortionists and 'benders'.

And their outrage worked. In 1889 the Prevention of Cruelty to Children Act was introduced, making it illegal for children under ten to be in a street, public house, circus or place of entertainment, playing or singing for profit. Children over seven years of age were, however, still allowed to appear in pantomimes.

In 1894 the act went a step further and any person procuring a child under the age of sixteen to be trained as an acrobat, contortionist, circus performer or for any dangerous exhibition was liable to a fine of twenty five pounds or three months imprisonment.

Chapter Fourteen

THE HIPPODROME

1888 Monday 9th July

Mrs Blair is doing a roaring trade. Her London natives sold out by midday, her New York blue points have been reduced to a pile of empty shells and her stew pots have been washed out a dozen times over. The visitors, it seems, can't get enough of her oysters. Even the new barrel delivered this afternoon will need replenishing before the day is out or she'll be dishing up cockles and whelks like she did yesterday. Who would have thought the season would turn out like this?

A few months back Annie Blair was anticipating only passing trade from boatmen, porters and drivers waiting at the car stand on the Parade. But then an enormous wooden building began to take shape on the empty yard in Bath Place, directly opposite her oyster shop. All of a sudden she felt as though she'd been given a golden ticket.

Rumour had it that the building was going to be a circus. A circus, would you believe! Mind you, it's hard to keep pace with all the building going on in this part of Douglas. A new pier, an extension to the new pier, new promenades, new dining establishments, new hotels, new shops. Not too long ago Bath Place was just a narrow, cramped corner of old Douglas filled with decrepit houses, coal yards, smithies and fish dealers. Then the Victoria Pier was built and soon every man and his wife had to squeeze through these narrow streets to get to and from the railway station. Until a couple of years ago, that is, when the Town Commissioners bought the yard on Bath Place so they could widen the road. The shabby old properties were torn down, the area was opened up and, as providence would have it, Annie Blair now finds herself on the Island's front doorstep.

Someone else whose fortunes are on the turn thanks to Bath Place is James Elphinstone, the driving force behind the construction of the new building. James is the flamboyant proprietor of the Gaiety Theatre and normally at this juncture of the season his schedule of plays and recitals would be in full swing. But the theatre's been closed for months at the behest of the Town Commissioners for remedial works (to comply with some fiddle-faddle new safety law) and there's little sign of it re-opening any time soon. A new business in Bath Place could put him back on the road to a comfortable retirement.

Not that James Elphinstone knows a great deal about circus. In truth, it's all something of a gamble. Now in his seventh decade his life has largely centred around theatre. In his youth he dazzled audiences with his powerful stage performances (his Othello is still talked about in The Potteries) and latterly he's enjoyed great success as a theatre manager, running businesses in both England and the Isle of Man over the last decade. But the world of entertainment is ever-changing and it's always wise to keep an eye on the competition. Circus has traditionally done well here and the only visiting company lined up to visit this summer has been delayed, so why shouldn't he fill the gap? This evening, when the doors open for the first time on his purpose-built hippodrome, he will find out if his gamble has paid off.

He's certainly had to play clever. Some of the Town Commissioners made it clear from the start they wanted the yard in Bath Place to remain empty while they decided its long-term future. Others favoured using it for ladies' lavatories, left-luggage offices and waiting rooms. James offered them another option – go ahead with the proposed facilities, in the corner nearest the pier, but rent him the remainder on which to erect a small circus for just one or two seasons. If constructed of wood, the circus could easily be dismantled at short notice. A new recreational attraction near the pier would help cater for the three hundred thousand pleasure seekers expected to visit the island this year, a busy part of town would gain decent facilities, his rent payments would bolster town funds and, more importantly, he would stay in business.

James wasted no time in getting together solid figures to back his proposal. In April, as spring tides crashed against the high wall that protects the eastern side of Bath Place yard from the Irish Sea, he met on site with an architect recommended for his expertise in circus design. E.T.Harrison, of Southport, has worked for some of the biggest names in the business during his long career - George Sanger, William Batty, the Cookes &c. – and, despite his advanced age, is still designing up to four circus buildings per year.

The two men hunched into their overcoats, battling to stay warm, as a bitterly cold wind swirled around the empty yard. Not the ideal meeting place for a man with a bronchial chest but James listened intently, trying not to cough, as Mr Harrison explained his plans. His idea was for a striking, octagonal hippodrome, constructed entirely of wood, built in two tiers with a small, vented cupola on top. The large bottom tier would include a standard forty-two feet diameter ring surrounded by generous pit seating and numerous rows of grandstand seating encircled by a wide raised promenade with gallery seating above. The smaller top tier would be fitted out with all the necessaries for lighting, rigging and ventilation. Despite its compact appearance the building would comfortably accommodate up to two thousand people, all with an excellent view, at every performance. By incorporating the stables and necessary offices into the building beneath the promenade, the hippodrome would require a total of only about a thousand square yards of land.

James Elphinstone nodded enthusiastically. Despite the weather, as he looked around the empty yard he sensed nothing but opportunity. Upper Church Street has had its day as a circus location, of that he is convinced, whereas on this footing, at the base of the new pier, he should easily be able to drum up two thousand people a night.

Even the high sea wall sheltering the two men from the wind and salt spray could prove very useful. The Town Commissioners have designated the wall as a posting station for giant hoardings up to thirty feet high, easily visible as boats approach the harbour. Visitors stepping off the steamers will be in no doubt as to the entertainments that await them.

And on every side of the yard there is potential. In the days before Bath Place was widened, the crush of conveyances waiting for steamers to arrive was often so intense that a line of cars would extend all the way down the Parade, around the Royal Hotel and onto the North quay, spilling into side streets and alleyways. Now, with all the extra space, a thousand cab licences have already been issued this season and the road circumventing the yard is crammed from morning till night with hackney carriages shining with new paint, their horses sporting polished harnesses, their registration brasses gleaming.

The front elevation of the circus will not only look onto Mrs Blair's oyster shop in Bath Place but will be mere feet away from the side entrance of the elegant Peveril Hotel. Guests enjoying an evening drink in the hotel lounge need only slip through the door and across the street to enjoy the antics of a clown or a dashing rider on horseback, while those staying in the south-facing corner rooms will wake to the sight of flags waving gaily on the circus roof. Even the area behind the Peveril offers James Elphinstone a source of prospective customers. The corner where Bath Place joins the Parade used to lead to a large shipyard worked by burly men with grimy faces.

Now the shipyard is gone and the shipwrights have been replaced by visitors shopping for herb beer, souvenir china and embroidered handkerchiefs on the marvellous new avenue, named after Governor Walpole, that stands in its stead.

But James Elphinstone's greatest stroke of fortune is the proximity of Bath Place yard to the new Promenade at the foot of the Victoria Pier. Every day throughout the summer this large open space in front of the Peveril Hotel is transformed into a dark, slowly moving river as thousands of people make their way to and from the steamers that bring them to the Island. The entrance to his circus will be one of the first sights new arrivals take in as their steamers berth at the Pier. Porters, car drivers and lodging house touts will ply their business in its shadow, and the horse trams that transfer visitors along the seafront will drop their passengers within yards of the circus box office. His new venture will, quite simply, be impossible to ignore.

Following their initial site meeting James Elphinstone urged Mr Harrison to draw up his plans without delay. Days later, in the Town Commissioners' boardroom in nearby Fort Street, large sheets of technical drawings were spread over the boardroom table. As Mr Harrison explained, the design replicates that of a typical American canvas 'big top', but is constructed using more substantial – and weather proof - materials. And Douglas may have seen circus buildings before, but never an octagonal one. This is modern, inventive architecture, based on proven designs of highly successful existing European circuses such as those in Copenhagen, Amien and Douai and not dissimilar, in fact, to the great Cirque d'Hiver in Paris!

On the second of May, the Town Commissioners agreed to rent the space to James Elphinstone for two hundred pounds per season. He could not have been more delighted. Within days he had a reputable building company engaged, a large labour force organised and a huge consignment of timber on order.

Annie Blair has also been taking a keen interest in the developments on Bath Place yard. In early spring she watched with great curiosity as two men in dark coats huddled in the lee of the high sea wall. Then, a short while later, one of the men, a distinguished looking chap of similar age to Mr Elphinstone, returned with complex-looking instruments and spent the morning taking measurements and scribbling in a large book. Soon after, a small army of workmen and boys turned up on the site in buffeting winds and driving rain and, under the watchful eye of the elderly gent and the well-known local builders Robert and John Cain, began marking out and digging a wide circle of foundations. By dinnertime on the first day the site had already been transformed. While the younger lads crouched behind the sea wall to unwrap packets of cheese and barley bread for their midday sustenance, the foremen and senior labourers downed tools and headed for Mrs Blair's oyster shop, lured by the smell of cooked shellfish and the promise of ale to wash it down. Annie Blair could not have been more delighted.

Days later large wagons began squeezing their way into Bath Place, loaded down with heavy iron scaffolding posts, and with Robert Cain shouting orders into the wind a giant metal structure gradually took shape, not unlike a colossal bird cage. Then the wood started to arrive, wagon after wagon of it, unloaded from the Scandinavian and American timber ships that fill Douglas harbour. Mr Harrison calculated the hippodrome would require a quantity of timber rarely seen in one building on the island and Robert Cain's army of labourers were soon busy carting no less than sixty thousand feet of floor boards, five thousand feet of sawn boards, four thousand feet of deals, plus a large quantity of scantlings, doors, posts and rails.

As June unfolded in unseasonably cold fine drizzle, the wooden building quickly began to take shape, layer upon layer of timber woven in ever smaller circles like a giant puzzle. Dozens of labourers and joiners dressed for hard work in dark worsted trousers, canvas jackets and flat caps, shovelled, heaved and hammered from dawn till dusk, swarming over the site like ants, whistling and cussing in their rush to get the job finished. And every day for six weeks, with rarely a break, the quiet figure of Mr Harrison has been observed on site, conferring with the foremen, taking measurements and checking his plans, watching the labourers as they balance high on narrow joists like sailors, casually manhandling cumbersome pieces of timber, unfazed by the gusts of wind blowing in off the sea.

By the end of June the exterior of the building was complete and days later, after an intense, round-the-clock effort by an experienced team of decorators, gas fitters, upholsterers and painters, the interior was also ready to be signed off. After six exhausting weeks Mr Harrison was finally able to take a break. On a calm July morning, as the sun broke through the clouds, he put down his instruments and took a short stroll to appreciate the vista spread out before him. For a man more used to bleak, urban panoramas the Douglas seascape was invigorating.

On the other side of the high sea wall there is a narrow strip of sand and stones that runs between the old Red Pier and the new Victoria Pier. Laundry maids had their linen laid out to dry and dozens of children darted around the small beach, skimming pebbles and looking for crabs in the rocks beneath the pier. At the base of the Promenade lines of empty, gaily painted rowing boats bobbed up and down on the choppy waters. But it was the vessels in the outer harbour and the bay that really drew Mr Harrison's eye. Local herring boats scooted across the water in every direction, their dark canvas sails fluttering in the wind like brown moths; low-slung paddle steamers thrashed their way into port trailing black plumes of smoke, and giant barges loaded with concrete blocks crossed from the cement works on Douglas Head to the new extension at the end of the pier, their wakes buffeting the penny ferries jam-packed with holidaymakers heading in the other direction to the attractions at the top of the Head.

In the middle of the bay, sitting quietly at the edge of all this activity, Mr Harrison could just make out the elegant lines of the steam yacht, the Santa Cecilia, the property of the Marquis of Anglesey. The yacht has been moored in the bay for the past week while its distinguished passengers take excursions on the Island. If Mr Harrison has judged Mr Elphinstone correctly he will no doubt be inviting the Marquis and his American wife and their guests to attend the opening night of the circus.

Early on the morning of the ninth of July, well before the box office is due to open, James Elphinstone's New Promenade Circus is finally revealed to the public, albeit with little pomp and ceremony. The grand opening will come later. For now, James has business to attend to. The first people through the door are a select group of news reporters invited for a special guided tour of the finished building while it is still pristine, dust-free and sparkling with new splendour.

The outside, the reporters note, is decidedly plain and unremarkable aside from its unusual shape and dimensions. But the interior is a revelation. The building has two entrances and the reporters are shown through a spacious porch leading to the pit, promenade and box seats. Their first impression is that of a grand country mansion. A pay office and doors marked for cloakrooms and conveniences are the only indication that this is not a private house. Classic statuary line the walls in bas-relief, brightly lit by an enormous chandelier that sparkles above a wide curved staircase leading to the promenade. As they climb the stairs James Elphinstone addresses the reporters in his most mellifluous tones on the importance of public safety. Safety, he stresses with great solemnity, is of the utmost priority. It is his determination to properly address such issues that has postponed the opening of his Gaiety Theatre this year and he is keen to avoid any similar problems with his circus. In the event of an emergency the whole building could be cleared in two minutes. Close attention has been paid to the width of the entrances and exits and all exterior doors open outwards.

On entering the auditorium the reporters' eyes are immediately drawn upwards to the vault-like ceiling by light flooding through the large vents in the top of the cupola, high above their heads. The main body of the room is still in half-darkness, the gas lamps cold and lifeless, but once their eyes adjust to the gloom the craftsmanship in the wooden structure becomes evident. Tens of thousands of precisely laid timber planks create the feeling of a cathedral, and the reporters' voices reverberate against the wood, making their skin prickle. Coloured, silken curtains hanging from rafters in the ceiling drift delicately in the slight breeze and thin shafts of light bounce off gilded mirrors attached to the eight quarter posts, intensifying the spiritual atmosphere.

Everywhere they look are signs of great attention to detail. From the intricate decorations around the promenade to the handsome glass globes on the gas lamps, it appears that no expense has been spared and no shortcuts taken. Such a high level of finesse in such a short time seems quite extraordinary.

Naturally, being a hippodrome, the reporters are anxious to see the stables and here again, innovation appears to be the order of the day. Running beneath the promenade, under a low ceiling, every inch of space has been put to good use. In a long, curved corridor following the outer perimeter of the building a well-organised harness room reveals row upon row of gleaming bridles and colourful saddle cloths. The corridor then continues as a long line of dimly-lit, straw-lined wooden stalls occupied by a variety of horses and ponies, solid, stocky beasts in a multitude of sizes and colours, tethered by chains affixed to the sides of the stalls. While some of them munch quietly on piles of hay, others rub their shiny rumps against the wooden partitions, or clatter and thump their hooves, shaking their heads in frustration. A thick, pungent smell of warm hides, animal breath and fresh dung hangs heavily in the confined space.

One of the equestrian performers returning from an early morning ride has to squeeze past the reporters while handing his horse to the head groom and pauses while they pump him with a barrage of questions. Yes, he agrees, the horses are pampered animals. But they're very different from brutish cart horses. A circus horse takes years of training and they do a lot of travelling. There isn't often time for proper rest so they have to eat well and be looked after or it will show in their performance. Horses are very good at reading a human's body language and a performing horse has to trust its trainer. They thrive on praise and endless patience. Pats, scratches behind the ears, rubbing the neck. Lots of contact, soft soothing words and treats. Sugar and carrots. The horse must understand the rider's voice and movements. The better the rider knows the horse and its personality the more they can achieve. And yes, an act with multiple horses brings its own challenges but horses are herd animals so if you can train one horse up well to perform in the ring it makes it more likely the others will follow their leader.

As for a circus rider, a good diet is important for them too! The training and performing is strenuous and you have to eat good food to give you energy but not so much that you carry too much weight. The heavier the rider the more strain on the animal's back and bones.

The reporters squint as they emerge into the daylight. Mr Elphinstone appears to have pulled off a remarkable coup. His building is novel and surprisingly commodious. Every comfort is catered for. And, judging by the performer they spoke to, his artistes are true professionals. If all goes well, tonight's opening should be a triumph.

As they leave the circus they are met by a large crowd which has gathered for the opening of the box office. On the stroke of eleven the shutters on the office are drawn up and a buxom woman appears behind the small counter, resplendent in a tall hat with a black ostrich feather in it. She has pitch black hair and eyes to match, rimmed with black kohl, and her cheeks are mottled with spidery red veins. In a voice edged with gravel she exhorts the waiting crowd to "step this way for tickets to the Home of Joy. Children under twelve half price to all parts except the gallery." The crowd surge forward and the reporters duck out onto the street.

By one o'clock, when the shutters are pulled down on the box office, virtually every seat in the reserved areas has been sold for tonight's opening performance. James Elphinstone feels like a man who can suddenly breathe again after being held under water. His hippodrome has been certified, his builders and architect will get paid and now his summer season can truly begin.

Of course, the real test will be judged by the quality of his acts. With only weeks to organise a full programme, James has spent many hours scouring the small advertisements in the 'Era', contacting agents and artistes, and securing, he hopes, an impressive line-up. Heading the bill tonight are the trick-riding Yelding brothers, Tom – the 'Newmarket Jockey' and Harry – the 'Continental Scene Act rider', and Tom's wife Emily, a thrilling young bare-back rider who goes by the name of 'Miss Emilene'. Tom and Emily were here back in '82 with Harmston's Circus but of course, at that time, the circus was in Upper Church street. Being near the pier will be a completely different experience for them.

As the afternoon unfolds, James Elphinstone's mood continues to improve. Where one person came to the Island a few years ago, now twenty come and despite the overcast skies and cold wind the promenade is crowded with itinerant singers, musicians and black-faced artists entertaining a dense melee of visitors with little better to do than wait for the circus doors to open. The rough seas are keeping them away from water-borne pursuits and dozens of idle boatmen in blue jerseys and top boots hang around the stone walls that edge the pier, smoking and chewing tobacco. All around them hotel porters weave their way through the press of bodies, pulling carts piled high with portmanteaus, boxes, trunks, hat-boxes and gun cases. In the height of summer the air in this part of Douglas usually carries the distinctive aroma of nearby curing yards and the sewage outfall but the breeze has spared today's crowd such un-pleasantries. The only obstacles they face are pickpockets and the persistent lodging house touts that hustle for their custom.

By half past six, with just half an hour until the doors are due to open on the New Promenade Circus, Annie Blair is also thankful for the inclement weather. Her last barrel of oysters is almost empty. The pile of shells in the back alley is the size of a small pig-sty and the customers in the saloon bar behind her shop are in full song. Every booth in the saloon has been occupied throughout the day and a thick haze of cigarette and pipe smoke hovers beneath the stained yellow ceiling, mingling with the tangy whiff of fish offal that leaches into the room from the kitchens and the backyard.

Her customers today are mostly northern working folk, nondescript in dark tweed, their trouser hems frayed and dirty and their bowler hats stained and battered. The women wear shawls and straw bonnets trimmed with tired silk flowers. But they sing with all the gusto of people who don't have to get up for work in the morning and as they leave Mrs Blair's and head over the road to join the crush for the circus, some even deviate to have their portraits taken at Mr Pickup's portable photographic booth in Bath Place.

At seven o'clock on the dot James Elphinstone looks at his watch and instructs his doormen to open the doors. On the side giving access to the boxes he is on hand to welcome several parties of dignitaries. A large group are visiting from the yacht the Santa Cecilia and a handful of Douglas Town Commissioners have rushed here straight from their usual Monday evening meeting. At the other entrance there is almost a stampede as well over a thousand people push and shove their way into the porch, their enthusiasm undampened by the burly fellows employed to turn away drunkards and undesirables.

On entering the auditorium, however, they hesitate, just for a moment, before being swept along by the momentum of the crowd. The building seems huge, its vastness emphasised by the brilliant light shining from the side lamps on every pillar and a central chandelier fitted with thousands of starry jets. It is hard to believe this cavernous space is the same building as the one they have seen from the outside. Surely, they are victims of some clever magician. The strangeness of it all is emphasised by the eerie whooshing sound of the wind blowing through the top vents in the cupola. But as the auditorium fills, the wind is soon drowned out by a swell of voices and laughter that echoes around the circular walls.

After declaring Mr Elphinstone's circus officially open and welcoming the dignitaries, the ringmaster wastes little time on the usual hyperbole. The crowd have barely sat down before the ring curtain is drawn aside and a handsome, sixteen hands high, white mare thunders into the ring followed by an athletic young man dressed as a sailor who runs alongside it. The horse is solid and stocky and wears only a thick pad on its broad back, a coating of rosin on its rump and a taut rein that runs from its bridle to its girth, keeping its neck elegantly arched and its head steady. As the animal settles into a smooth canter the ringmaster guides it with his long whip to keep it as close as possible to the edge of the ring and the man – none other than Thomas Yelding – leaps in one bound from the ground onto the horse's back.

In the familiar mode of the circus 'jockey' Tom balances on the horse without the aid of his hands and, standing with his feet either side of the horse's spine, he completes a circuit of the ring with ease, his body erect yet relaxed, his waves to the crowd met with loud hollering and whistling. As the horse begins its next lap Tom leans forward and raises one leg behind him, staying in that position for a full circuit, then returns to an upright position before lowering his body until he is kneeling on the horse's back, from where he jumps to a standing position and suddenly somersaults from the back of the horse to the ground. The crowd love it. The band raises its tempo and the pounding of the horse's hooves resonates around the wooden building, rippling through the timbers. A confident display of vaulting follows, in a variety of permutations, before a fresh horse is brought into the ring and set to a fast canter.

The audience watch eagerly as a clown enters the circle and produces a red scarf which he ties in a blindfold over Tom's eyes. The ringmaster urges the crowd to silence – or as good as he can muster – and Tom bows his head and appears to be listening to the sound of the horse as it moves around the ring. As the horse completes its first circle and crosses in front of Tom he runs after it and leaps onto its back as though propelled by some unseen elastic rope, alighting on its rump with extraordinary precision. The crowd hold their breath as he struggles to establish his balance but he quickly adjusts to the movement of the horse and deftly undoes the blindfold, raising his arms in acknowledgement of the crowd's appreciation.

As he leaves the ring he passes a young woman standing on the back of a pretty piebald mare and the two performers nod to each other, smiling. 'Miss Emiliene' is dressed in the costume of a bonny fishwife, plump with layers of woollen plaid, a scarf round her head and a dirty apron tied round her middle. With her horse moving steadily beneath her she pantomimes throwing rubber fish from her apron pocket into the amused audience and slicing the air with a filleting knife, before making a show of divesting herself of her outer layers of clothing to reveal the wretched outfit of a young waterman, complete with long pole handed up by the clown. She finishes by gleefully throwing off her dirty rags to reveal the tartan kilt, fly plaid and sporran of Rob Roy, the Scottish folk hero. The audience don't quite know what to make of the sight of a young woman dressed like a Highlander but her animated performance, on the back of a moving horse, is certainly something to tell their friends.

In the velvet-lined comfort of the box seats James Elphinstone confers with the Town Commissioners who have joined him as guests for the night. His ever-present cough is exacerbated by the fine white dust that fills the air but their obvious enjoyment of the programme and compliments about his building make it all worthwhile.

The evening is brought to a close with a mesmerising performance by Tom Yelding's younger brother Harry. Harry is not only a skilled bareback rider but a natural comedian with a leaning to the grotesque. He has a scenic act lined up for this Douglas crowd that he is sure will appeal to all tastes and ages.

At a nod from the ringmaster the ring fills with members of the company – clowns, riders, acrobats – all in full costume, lively and radiating energy beneath the white lights, skipping, tumbling and waving to the audience. And then a small, dejected figure enters the melee, sitting backwards on a trotting pony, dressed in rags and holding out an empty bowl. The company draw into the middle of the ring to give him space and it soon becomes clear that this is Mr Dickens' famous creation, the poor orphan Oliver Twist. But not for long. As the pony reaches the ring curtain the 'boy' jumps down and flings himself up onto a bigger horse that has been sent into the ring. Hurling his rags aside and adopting a humorous, dower countenance he now appears in the funereal black of Mr Sowerberry, Dickens' undertaker. Then he is thrown a handful of garments and, quick as a flash, he has changed again, swaggering on the back of the horse in the impudent manner of the Artful Dodger, complete with over-large top hat, silk cravat, vest and long coat. Every adult and child in the audience now cottons on to what is being played out before them and they laugh and clap in time to the beat of the horse's hooves.

Following on from the Artful Dodger, Harry produces a fine, hand-wringing impersonation of Fagin, the gang master, resplendent in red wig and beard and long carpet coat, before seamlessly metamorphosing into Fagin's rough associate Bill Sykes, for whom he dispenses with the red hair and takes up a cudgel. But it is his closing representation of Mr Bumble, the cruel, bloated, workhouse Beadle, in blue velvet state coat and cocked hat, that has the audience in stitches. Here is a pompous bully who delights in the misery of others but is shown up as a coward. Factory workers in the audience take great delight in seeing Harry Yelding reduce him to a figure of mockery.

By ten o'clock the New Promenade Circus has been declared a resounding success. James Elphinstone is to be congratulated and the Town Commissioners pump his hand enthusiastically as he bids them goodnight. The circus takes a while to empty and it's nearly midnight by the time the performers depart for their lodgings and the grooms can settle the horses. The woman on the ticket booth is last to leave, having counted the ticket stubs while nursing a large glass of porter and stout.

Once the auditorium falls silent, a night watchman goes around the deserted spectator stands gathering up litter and dampening down the dust with cans of water. The following morning, as the sun begins to rise, he sweeps the loam into buckets and runs a wet rag over the rails in readiness for a new day of rehearsal and performance.

Meanwhile, in a nearby hotel, an elderly gent is hastily packing his trunk in preparation for catching the early morning steamer. Mr Harrison did not attend Mr Elphinstone's opening night as he has a commitment to a circus project for the Sangers in Yorkshire and, feeling his age, feared being over-tired for the journey. He will have to be content to read the critics' opinions in the newspaper columns.

After a last check around his room, he shrugs on his dark coat and derby hat, carefully folds up his plans and notebooks and places them in his portmanteau, then steps out onto the street where he's quickly enveloped by the throng heading for the Victoria Pier.

Addendum

In mid-July the New Promenade Circus engaged the well-known side saddle rider Nellie Reid from the Royal Aquarium in London to ride her high-jumping horse Sydney over gates, hurdles, stone walls and a fully set dinner table.

Unfortunately, the sheer volume of people attending the circus attracted problems. In August the town commissioners raised complaints about the disgraceful litter in Bath Place, caused chiefly by the people coming out of the Circus, and suggested that Mr Elphinstone should place a lamp there after dark. It also led to an unsavoury incident when two men who'd spent the evening at the circus were charged with pushing a visitor into the adjacent harbour at low tide, resulting in the man sustaining two broken legs and a severe head injury. Both men were committed for trial.

There was also a near fatality in the circus itself. As a sword swallower swung his long sword prior to putting it down his throat, it flew out of his hand and into the audience, striking a woman with a child in her arms. Fortunately, she was struck by the flat part of the sword causing little injury but a great deal of audience excitement.

As the month drew to a close, inmates of the Douglas House of Industry were invited to the circus, free of charge, by the proprietor Mr Elphinstone. They all enjoyed the entertainment and warmly thanked Mr Elphinstone for such a kindly treat.

Circus architect E.T.Harrison hardly paused for breath following his time in the Isle of Man, spending the next few months overseeing the construction of a large hippodrome for Sangers Circus. However, his heavy work load took its toll and he passed away the following March, aged seventy, at his home in Lancashire. His large collection of circus plans was promptly offered for sale to circus proprietors, circus architects and builders.

James Henry Elphinstone died in September 1892 at the Douglas residence of his son George, his heart weakened by chronic bouts of bronchitis. His obituary noted that, by his death, Douglas had lost a valuable citizen, an active businessman, conscientious, honest and approachable, who was always very much respected by his employees.

Annie Blair's house in Bath Place was put up for sale in October 1894, the shop being let separately. The auctioneer waxed lyrical about the superb location of the property as a place to catch visitors and roused laughter when he noted that the only stock necessary for the shop was a knife, some vinegar and black pepper.

Tom Yelding continued thrilling audiences with his bare-back riding well into the next decade, and later ran his own circus in Merthyr Tydfil, Wales. His daughter Lizzie also gained a reputation as one of the world's best female bare-back riders, said to be the only woman who could mount a galloping horse from the ground. In 1900 Tom and Lizzie sailed with their prized horses to South Africa and engagements in Pretoria.

Chapter Fifteen

THE INDIAN PAVILION

1891 Wednesday 5th August

A lively group of young boys darts between rows of flowerbeds, whooping loudly and hollering 'ho-ka-hey!' in high-pitched voices. One of the boys brandishes a piece of wood like a tomahawk, startling the couples and families enjoying an early evening stroll through the Belle Vue Pleasure Ground. The boys dodge around the shrubs that line the pathway and head for the bandstand, circling it twice before racing off in the direction of the bear pit, leaving a swirling cloud of discarded sweet packets in their wake.

The air is warm and still and long after the boys have vanished from sight their exuberant war cries resonate around the pleasure ground, blending with a rich backdrop of strange and intriguing noises - a deep, drawn-out rumble, a chorus of loud shrieks and simian chattering and a continuous hum of human voices.

The boys' energy is somewhat remarkable considering the day they have had. Belle Vue is set in a lush river valley a mile west of Douglas and the boys left home early to ensure they would arrive in time for the gates opening at ten. On the main road out of town they were accompanied by hundreds of other people walking in the same direction – children, some with parents and some without, young lovers, errant clerks, carefree holidaymakers - passed along the way by an omnibus ferrying less able-bodied passengers to and from the hotels on the seafront. As Belle Vue came into sight the crowd began to slow and thicken, and it wasn't until well after ten that the boys were able to hand over their sixpences at the turnstile and push their way in.

Since then they have spent the day in a whirlwind of activity. Running races and playing cricket, splashing around in boats, hooting on the switchback railway and laughing at the antics of the mischievous monkeys, a morose brown bear and two happy, clapping seals. But it is the circus in the Indian Pavilion that has fired their boyish imaginations. A Red Indian war chief, thundering around the ring on his steaming charger, fringes and feathers flying. A giant, ponderous elephant performing funny tricks. A female devil on horseback. A young tightrope walker and a juggling princess on a giant snowball. So many mind-boggling acts it is hard to remember them all. And all so very thrilling. The sixpence admission fee to the gardens includes a section of free seats at both the afternoon and evening shows in the circus and as soon as it is open again, the boys will be there, jostling for a place.

Meanwhile, they have time to fill and make their way to the refreshment saloon beyond the Pavilion. A long line of people snakes out of the building, fanning themselves against the heat and swarms of midges.

As the boys take their place at the back of the line they become aware of unusual activity behind the Pavilion, by the stable doors. The men in the line have turned to stare, while the women look the other way. A handful of flaxen-haired young women dressed only in sleeveless bodices, satin trunks, flesh-coloured tights and calf-length boots are gathered around a two-wheeled Safety bicycle, holding the machine and its rider steady. As the boys watch mesmerized, one of the girls leaps lightly up onto the shoulders of the rider and tucks her legs beneath the rider's armpits. The girls holding the bicycle let go and the rider edges slowly forward, her face a study in concentration. Her companions clap and laugh as she bumps across the grass. In the cool shade a man watches them, idly smoking a cigarette, half-dressed in baggy trousers held up with braces and a yellowed vest, his pale neck and chest bare, his expression masked by garish face paint.

The line into the refreshment saloon suddenly begins moving and the boys lose sight of the circus performers as they're swept along by the crowd through an entrance foyer lush with tall green ferns and spiky palms. The foyer leads into a cavernous dining room, hot and sticky from the crush of bodies and steam pumping out of giant hot-water urns. The Belle Vue is run along strict temperance lines and tea is served here by the gallon. Hundreds of people sit jammed together at linen-covered, iron-framed tables, their excited voices mingling with the clatter of cups and saucers. In front of them are plates and dishes piled high with ham and bloater paste sandwiches, beef salads, cheese and pickles, rice pudding and currant buns.

The boys are served lemonade by young women in black dresses and starched white aprons, while an older woman – Mrs Johnson, the wife of the pleasure ground's proprietor – issues orders and keeps the line moving.

After tea the boys make one last circuit of the pleasure grounds before heading back to the Indian Pavilion. Belle Vue is, after all, a place that invites serious exploration. Over the past few years the Johnsons have been responsible for transforming over twenty acres of once swampy meadowland into a carefully-landscaped paradise, planted with trees, shrubs and swathes of grass. Two picturesque rivers, the Dhoo and the Glass, converge in the centre of the grounds before flowing as one broad waterway towards Douglas harbour.

The boys zigzag through the gardens, crossing numerous ornamental bridges until they reach a vast, shallow boating lake with a small island at its centre. Even here, at the furthest perimeter of the estate, the Pavilion is clearly visible – its colourful minarets and domes standing proud above the gardens, as magical as a Maharajah's palace in a storybook. Elaborately decorated square towers at each corner of the rectangular building are topped with striped, onion-shaped crowns. In the middle, a pyramidal corrugated iron roof, gaily painted in red and white like a circus tent, is capped with a giant dome-shaped cupola coated in lustrous zinc.

It's said that Mr Johnson bought the Pavilion from the famous English naturalist William Cross, who built it as a means of displaying his collection of exotic animals and real-life Indian natives at the 1886 Liverpool Exhibition.

Once the exhibition had finished Mr Cross sold the building and animal cages and Mr Johnson – an energetic and enterprising young man - had the entire structure shipped over to the Isle of Man and rebuilt, retaining the monkey house in the rear of the building and modifying the rest of the interior to accommodate a circus.

The monkey house faces inwards to the pleasure ground and the boys have to pass by in order to reach the main Pavilion entrance on the opposite side. A strong earthy smell and loud screeching greets them even before its tall iron bars come into view. It's feeding time and a crowd has gathered to watch a keeper deliver buckets of fruit and vegetable scraps to the dozen occupants, who poke orange peel through the bars to the crowd's amusement.

To the boy's slight disappointment, the Pavilion at close quarters is not quite the exotic wonder it appears to be from a distance. The colourful minarets are little more than solid panels decorated with chiaroscuro to simulate windows, the striped domes are mottled with dull patches and the wooden walls could do with a lick of fresh paint. But the evening circus performance is about to begin and the noisy punters gathered by the entrance are concerned only with the dramas inside the building. Even as they wait there comes a loud thumping and shrill trumpeting from deep within and they exchange excited looks. Then, just five minutes before the doors are opened, all eyes turn to a large balloon which has been inflated on the grass nearby. A gentleman in a striking red and gold suit hops into the basket of the balloon and, at the burst of a bugle, he casts off the ropes and disappears up into the sky. The crowd exclaim in unison and burst into spontaneous applause.

The boys have already been through the Pavilion doors once today but the imposing entrance still makes them feel small and slightly overwhelmed. Inside, where once stood a replica Indian village complete with snake-charmers and tom-tom players, there is a now a circus ring softly lit from above by coloured-glass domes in the ceiling that play a kaleidoscope of different hues upon the sawdust. And there is a musky, dark, animal odour that lingers in the nose. The whole arena has an exotic air, quite different to any circus they have been to before.

Nearly every seat is taken and the boys squeeze into the back row of the free section. The view is not the best – they have to crane their necks to see round the pillars - and they are painfully close to the voluble twenty-piece circus band, but they are still happy to be here and dutifully rise to their feet as the band strikes up the National Anthem.

Just after seven thirty a man enters the ring, introducing himself as Professor Henry, the manager of the establishment. His appearance is unusually intimidating for a ring master, his dress being dark and severe. A peaked soldier's cap tops an outfit of dark collarless jacket emblazoned with medals, military trousers and steel-tipped cowboy boots, and in his right hand he carries a long thin cane. However, he assures the audience in enthusiastic tones that tonight they are to be treated to a marvellous programme of rational amusement that will both educate and entertain. They will see sights never before seen on this island, and experience thrills like nothing they have experienced before!

A blood-curdling scream and sinister rattling sound drive home his words. A dark-skinned man leaps into the ring and runs around the circle, shaking a hollow gourd at the audience. Pauba, the North American Chieftain, lives up to every preconception the boys have of the Indians of the Wild West. Black eyes stare out of a dark face, his features partly obscured by daubs of red and white paint. On his head he wears an extravagant war bonnet of long, black-tipped white feathers sewn onto a beaded headband from which hang white ermine tails and leather thongs strung with beads. Gold earrings dangle from his ears, and around his neck he wears a beaded choker and a necklace of shells, bone buttons and animal teeth. His tatty animal-skin vest is trimmed with fur and fringes, metal cuffs circle his buckskin shirt-sleeves and, to complete the look, he wears khaki trousers trimmed with red and white braid and leather moccasins.

After a circuit of the ring that has the audience cowering in their seats, Pauba dispenses with his head dress and gourd and whistles in the direction of the ring curtain. A magnificent bay horse gallops into the circle, loose stirrups banging against its sides. Pauba runs after it and in one clean movement leaps onto its back and rises into a standing position on its bouncing rump. Shaking his fists in the air and uttering war whoops, shrieks and yelps, he swoops confidently around the ring, black hair flying, before dropping to a sitting position and swivelling around to face backwards for a full circuit. He then turns again and appears to fall off the moving horse, but clings on with one leg, his whole body hanging parallel to the horse's body. The audience applaud vigorously and unconsciously sit forward.

His next move is observed with intense interest. Bimbo the clown has entered the ring and is nonchalantly picking up imaginary litter from the sawdust as Pauba, playing dead, hangs loosely from his saddle as the horse continues to thunder round the ring. As the clown comes nearer Pauba reaches into his belt for a tomahawk and once Bimbo is within reach attempts to surprise him by striking out with his weapon. Bimbo, however, apparently unaware of impending danger, spots something on the ground and ducks his head at the last minute, prompting the audience to convulse with relieved laughter. With a cry of 'Ho-ka-hey!' Pauba pulls himself upright into the saddle, startling the dim clown, and chases him from the ring.

In a triumphant gesture Pauba stands up in his wide leather stirrups, leaning sharply forward over the horse's lathered neck and waves his tomahawk in the air as the exhausted animal slows to a steady canter. In the warm fug of the auditorium the smell of perspiring bodies and horse sweat is intense and cloying. The boys on the back row of the stands jump up from their seats, whooping and hollering.

The acts that follow are gentle by comparison but nonetheless entertaining. Bimbo returns for an entrée on stilts, a female performer pleases the ladies in the crowd with the antics of her four small, well-trained ponies, and a ventriloquist provokes plenty of laughter with his curious talking doll. Then it is again time for something more exotic.

With a dramatic drum roll the ring curtain is pulled aside and a long, grey protuberance uncurls, sniffing the air. The audience come alive, pointing and sniggering. As the band launches into a heavy, pounding melody the rest of the creature slowly emerges into the light. The protuberance belongs to a large cumbersome elephant which clumps heavily into the ring, ankle chains clanking, its grey wrinkled body partially hidden beneath a richly embroidered red and gold blanket. Sitting comfortably astride its massive neck is the circus manager Professor Henry who waves to the audience and is joined, after a tap on the elephant's flank, by loud trumpeting which brings gales of laughter and loud applause. Most of the audience have never seen an exotic animal at such close quarters and they are nervous and spellbound in equal measure.

As the elephant reaches the centre of the ring the Professor slides deftly to the ground and both man and beast bow to the stands. The elephant dominates the auditorium, in both sheer physical size and aura. Here, on a small island in the middle of the Irish Sea, is a creature from the jungles of India. An alien beast of travellers' tales and foreign legends. It is easily a foot taller than its trainer and as solid as three cart horses put together, yet the mottled pale pink patches on its small ears and trunk give it a childlike vulnerability, an impression emphasised by the long black lashes that frame its doleful brown eyes.

The elephant is introduced as Sheriff, a close, faithful companion of the Professor's, with a hearty appetite - an elephant of his size can apparently consume three sacks of vegetables, four bundles of hay, twenty loaves of bread, buns, biscuits and dainties and gallons of milk in just one day! On cue, Bimbo the clown appears, bearing a large cabbage which he places at the elephant's feet before scampering from the ring. As the Professor educates the audience on the habits of Asiatic elephants, Sheriff picks up the cabbage with its trunk and shovels it into its pink, gaping mouth, chomping noisily and nodding its head.

The Professor is still talking when the creature finishes eating and doesn't see it curl its trunk towards a brass bell placed on a nearby table. Picking up the bell with surprising delicacy, it proceeds to give it a rigorous jangle. Bimbo re-enters, groaning under the weight of armfuls of cabbages, greens and loaves of bread, prompting the audience to loud guffaws. But when the clown prepares to deposit the food at the elephant's feet the Professor waves his arms in irritation and on cue the elephant gently shoves Bimbo out of the ring with its bulging head, receiving a surreptitious bun for its trouble. Having devoured the treat the elephant casually raises its tail and deposits a huge pile of steaming brown dung onto the sawdust, much to the amusement of the younger members of the audience.

The rest of the performance belongs entirely to the elephant and its trainer. Using only his cane and his voice the Professor encourages the creature to stand on its hind legs, to sit on a chair, to place its trunk in his hand and dance. For an animal weighing almost five tons its movements are astonishingly graceful. Only once does it stray from its routine, when some children on the front row throw biscuits into the circle but the biscuits are reduced to crumbs before the Professor has even noticed.

On the whole Sheriff is a huge success. Although a handful of delicate spectators find its massive presence – and odorous bowel movements – unsettling, the majority love its docile demeanour and clumsy attempts to perform tricks. When it lumbers from the ring, small ears flapping and ankle chains jangling, a thousand hands flutter in delight.

And then, abruptly, before the audience have time to catch their breath, the scene before them changes. From calm, ponderous grey to shocking, fiery red. A piebald horse bursts into the circle, the scarlet vision on its back causing every full-blooded male to lean forward, mouths agape. A slim, shapely young woman in a dazzling, close-fitting bright red bodysuit topped with a red, horned hood and red cape is seated bare-back upon the cantering horse, urging it to even greater speed. For the next ten minutes the renowned trick rider Madame Nita Palmyra has the audience a-gasp at her vivacity and devilment as she performs the thrilling Ride of Mephistopheles, a demonic, frantic descent to the hellish centre of the earth. She leaps, she hangs, she balances, she spins, her cape whirling around her. The temperature beneath the soft coloured lights of the pavilion, already warm, is suddenly stifling. Men loosen their shirt collars and remove their hats, while many of the women in the audience squirm uncomfortably.

Fortunately, Professor Henry is adept at managing an audience. As soon as Mme Palmyra has left the ring, he announces a whole new set of varieties, to suit every taste. A youthful high wire artiste is next to perform, followed by the clever ventriloquist. And then it is the turn of another talented young woman, as dainty in her demeanour as Nita Palmyra was audacious.

Madame Eva is young, elegant and dressed all in white. She enters the ring dancing, twirling an open parasol and posing to the audience with pointed, naked toes. A utility man comes behind her, rolling a giant canvas-covered white ball which he places in the centre of the circle. In a single effortless bound Eve leaps up onto the ball, standing erect and smiling widely as she launches into tiny steps that keep the ball moving backward and forward. Throughout, her eyes never leave the audience. With arms outstretched she proceeds to walk the 'animated snowball' around the ring, twirling the parasol, her body moving sinuously, at times teetering and stumbling but always quickly regaining her balance. The ball, a hollow wooden sphere, echoes as it rumbles around the sawdust. The spangled white costume that covers her slim frame shimmers under the lights. After the first circuit, to 'oohs' and 'aahs', she closes the parasol and tosses it to Bimbo the clown, waiting on the sidelines, who in turn throws her three clubs which she juggles while still moving her feet rapidly on top of the ball. In a moment of carelessness, one of the clubs drops to the ground but she carries on as though nothing has happened, smiling broadly.

After finishing with the clubs Eva tosses them back to the clown who successively passes her a set of balls, then three tall glass bottles and, to an intake of breath from the audience, a set of long knives, all of which are deftly thrown and caught to a backdrop of dramatic music as the outsize ball jiggles back and forth. Finally, to the delight of the boys in the back row of the free section, a man - who looks uncannily like the ventriloquist - enters the ring carrying three flaming torches which he passes carefully up to Madame Eva. As a hush falls over the audience, she launches one into the air, followed by another, and then another, while her feet continue to tap an urgent dance on the top of the ball. Tongues of flame and bright sparks whirl about her head as she juggles the torches, painting the air with rainbows of fire that cast an orange glow on her white costume.

Following Madame Eva's display there is a short interval during which many of the crowd escape to the foyer for some much-needed air. Those that remain in their seats are entertained by Bimbo the clown. As he happily plays the fool on the ringfence, other performers return to the ring, anonymously dressed in dark working outfits. With practised ease they quickly cover the sawdust with a large tarpaulin and drag in large frames of wood and metal, slotting them together to make a series of ramps attached to a small platform.

After fifteen minutes the audience troop back into the auditorium and seat themselves, re-invigorated. The band strike up a lively melody and to a smattering of polite applause the next act is introduced. The craze for bicycling has now, it seems, extended to the circus.

When the Silvani troupe of bicyclists pedal into the ring the boys recognise the four youngest as the artistes who were rehearsing at the back of the Pavilion although here, prettily dressed in full costume, their blonde hair stylishly coiffured, they are transformed from giggling girls into charismatic, confident beauties. An older couple, Madame and Monsieur Silvani, appear to be in charge of the routine and lead the girls around the ring, waving cheerfully with their free hands. Their bicycles are certainly splendid machines, silver-plated and patently expensive with strong tyres and matching-sized wheels. Though whether a steel contraption can measure up to the thrills offered by a steaming, galloping four-legged horse is clearly questionable in the minds of some of the audience, who snort derisively.

The majority, however, are transfixed by the unusual display unfolding before them. Eerie bands of coloured light sweep around the auditorium, generated by the Badoura lanterns fitted to the handlebars of each bicycle. The perforated tin globes, lined with patterned linen and lit from within by a carriage candle, create a magical and picturesque effect reminiscent of the Arabian nights. The girls' costumes glitter and twinkle in the subdued light and ladies in the audience dressed in the season's fashionable silver-grey and white are transformed into visions of pink, green and gold.

Having softened the mood, the troupe gradually build up to their pièce de résistance. Pulling up the front wheels of their bicycles they ride round the ring on their back wheels, bringing hearty applause. Three performers then jump down and hop up onto the shoulders of the remaining three for another circuit. The whole troupe then ride up the ramps to the raised platform where they use the bicycles as acrobatic props, standing on the seats, sitting on the handlebars and sitting facing backwards. At one point Monsieur Silvani holds the handlebars of his bicycle and places his head on the seat, raising his legs in the air. Even the most cynical members of the audience have to agree it's all rather marvellous.

To finish, the riders descend from the platform, which is quickly dismantled and removed as they keep circling the ring fence. Once the circle is empty they line up side by side, three facing one way and three the other, blonde heads bobbing, and launch into a fast, perfectly symmetrical spin around the ring, the light and colour from their Badoura lanterns creating the effect of a giant Catherine wheel. The crowd is utterly captivated. At least half of them have fallen in love.

It has been a long night and many of the audience are visibly wilting but there is still more to come. A 'black-faced' comedian - who occasionally slips into a Scots accent – stirs them to laughter with his negro songs and ditties. A slick-haired Italian shocks with his daring on the high wire and yet another clever horseman pounds around the ring before the programme concludes. By eleven o'clock the kaleidoscope of entertainment inside the Indian Pavilion is finally at an end.

It's dark by the time the boys leave the circus and they emerge into a fairy bower. Against an indigo sky, bright arc lamps shine down on the gardens like giant moons and the flowerbeds and pathways are brilliantly illuminated by thousands of coloured fairy lamps suspended from the railings, which glow like gem stones. Behind them the Indian Pavilion is softened and jewel-like, its shabby paintwork rendered whole again by the strange light. Did the boys dream the fierce Indian warrior, the intelligent elephant, the lady in white juggling with fire? Were they real or merely fabulous fantasies? They leave the pleasure ground as they arrived, swept up in a surge of bodies, and stumble along the dark road back to Douglas, their heads full of wonder.

Addendum

Belle Vue experienced varying fortunes over subsequent years. In November 1891 it was the venue for a Hollantide Fair attended by farmers seeking to hire new labour. The police noted that without liquor on sale they'd never known such a well-behaved fair. Eight thousand people attended the fair, and every elementary school child was admitted free of charge and given a 'fairing' consisting of a piece of plum cake. The bear pit and monkey house were extremely popular.

In June 1892 Belle Vue was transformed into an impressive venue for the Isle of Man International Exhibition. New buildings were added to house trade exhibits from all over the world and the entire complex was illuminated by electric light. The circus entertainment continued, with a special steamer laid on to bring part of the Hippodrome and Circus company from Liverpool.

By the following summer Belle Vue was being advertised as the largest place of amusement on the Island, with grounds able to accommodate twenty thousand people and buildings to accommodate ten thousand. The eastern wing of the buildings that had housed the exhibition was filled with an aviary of exotic birds and caravan cages housing Wombwell's No.1 Royal Menagerie of performing lions, tigers, elephants, monkeys, hyenas, leopards, camels and a solitary pipe-smoking chimpanzee.

In the Indian Pavilion the stars of the show were the Yelding family of circus equestrians. Tom Yelding's finest act involved lying across his galloping horse's back and picking up his eleven-year old daughter Lizzie before rising to his feet with the girl in his arms. His brother John convincingly adopted the persona of a North American Indian chief.

Visitors transported to the Belle Vue by omnibus received a fright one evening when the vehicle, which was being drawn by an elephant, spooked a passing horse as it lumbered up Prospect Hill. The horse bolted, knocking over a boy carrying a sandwich board, smashing the board.

To mark the end of Mr Henry's highly successful fourth season at Belle Vue Mrs Johnson provided a sumptuous supper in his honour in the refreshment rooms. During the evening his admirers presented him with a gold watch chain and a silver-mounted pipe.

By early 1894 Belle Vue was struggling to compete in a crowded entertainment market, largely due to its restrictions on the sale and consumption of alcohol, and the property was offered for sale by public auction. The property included twenty two acres of grounds, the pavilion including the circus and monkey house, the refreshment room and kitchens, picture galleries, a model dairy, a shooting gallery and jungle, a switchback, stables to accommodate eighty horses, a four acre lake, cycling and trotting track with cricket and football ground, a grandstand, hot houses and a full-sized model of Nelson's ship 'Victory'.

Sheriff the elephant and his trainer Professor Henry moved on around the country, appearing at various cities across the north of England.

In September 1895 the Liverpool naturalist and wild animal dealer William Cross married Ethel Chadwick, a wealthy widow who resided at Ravensdale Castle in the north of the Isle of Man.

Chapter Sixteen

THE ACROBATS

1894 Saturday 7th July

A two-headed man stands facing an imaginary audience. Or is it just one man in a grotesque costume? It's hard to tell in the dim early morning light of the auditorium but there appears to be only one pair of feet touching the ground.

The apparition starts to sway and with the movement comes music, the spirited strains of violins playing an Irish jig. As the tempo of the music builds, the figure begins to bob up and down like a seesaw and the light from the ceiling cupola brings a curious scenario into clear relief. In the centre of the circle two well-formed and distinctly individual men are locked together in a most unnatural position. One has his feet planted firmly on the ground and leans to his left, confidently playing a violin tucked firmly beneath his chin. The other man's legs and feet are braced across his companion's body like a sign over a shopkeeper's doorway, his tightened stomach muscles keeping his torso upright and enabling him to join in a duet with his own instrument. For a few minutes they tilt from side-to-side, perfectly balanced and completely in harmony, their cheerful facial expressions devoid of any strain or discomfort until an over-enthusiastic flourish brings their rehearsal to a premature end, spilling them to the ground, chests heaving, in a flurry of laughter and sawdust.

Meanwhile, on the other side of town, a man is lying in the bath, eyes closed. The bathroom window is open and, although the hour is early, he can hear loud voices in the street below. His son and daughters are discussing, with some passion, an element of tonight's show and the sound makes him wistful.

When he first visited this island he was still in his twenties, long-haired, filled with fire, and as lean and fit as a butcher's dog. His children were barely out of napkins. This month he turns forty, his back is crooked and his abundant curls have long since fallen to the barber's floor. But Joe Ohmy, the once 'glittering star of the air', has no regrets. His energies are now well employed managing his own successful circus in which his talented offspring are the core performers. And despite nagging injuries he can still conjure up his own unique brand of aerial magic when required. Only recently he dazzled the Duke of York at a special royal performance by fixing a cap to his head stuck with half a dozen large squibs, then whirling on a rope fastened high in the ceiling with coloured spumes of fire gushing from his head.

Joe quickly finishes his morning toilet, mindful of a busy day in prospect. The start of his company's summer engagement in Douglas coincided with the arrival of "the Queen's weather" – a welcome burst of warm sunshine to brighten the activities of July the fifth when the Manx people celebrate their national day. But the change in the weather is a mixed blessing. After a slow, damp start to the holiday season the steamers plying the Irish Sea have been packed to the gunwales in recent days, prompting all the pleasure resorts on the island to throw their doors open for business simultaneously.

For the second year running Joe has taken a lease on Elphinstone's 'New Promenade' circus building down by the Victoria Pier and his advance publicity boasts that he has brought with him a substantial company of forty acts and forty horses. Though, in truth, the audience may see forty acts but who's to say they're not the same performers appearing twice or even three times in different guises? It's an old ruse but a good one. Imagine if he really had to pay that large a company? He'd be bankrupt before the season was over!

As is their custom the Ohmy family have taken lodgings in Myrtle Street, opposite the site of the old circus in upper Douglas. The location is somewhat inconvenient, but Joe has been staying in this part of town since his first visit to the Isle of Man and it holds a nostalgic familiarity. Plus, their landlady is most obliging of their peculiar timekeeping and dietary requirements. The whole family usually breakfast together shortly after dawn, tucking into steaming bowls of porridge followed by an abundance of eggs, kippers, ham and chicken.

Today the town is already busy as the family make their way down to Bath Place and shoppers and shopkeepers call out to them as they walk down Victoria Street. The appearance of 'King Ohmy' is always a cheerful cause for celebration.

On entering the side door of the New Promenade Circus the family are met by infectious snatches of fiddle playing. In the darkened auditorium, illuminated only by thin shafts of light from the ceiling cupola, they can just make out two slim young men who appear to be locked together in a bizarre ritual, while managing to play a passable Irish dance melody. Other performers attempting to rehearse on the sidelines have stopped to watch but Joe Ohmy gives the pair only a cursory greeting before heading for the stables. The Lloyd Brothers are topping his bill tonight and he needs them to practise undistracted.

Not that James and Hugh Lloyd don't come with excellent credentials. Unlike most acrobats they really are birth brothers, the sons of one of Astley's veteran artistes. Now in their late twenties they've been performing together for a decade, honing their routines with the intuition that is enjoyed by close siblings. Their close attention to one another and response to each other's needs has seen them develop acts of rare ability. At today's performances they will present two distinct acts, firstly, in deference to their employer's wishes, under the nom-de-plume of the "Heeno Brothers" and then later in the programme under their own name.

As with all successful acrobats they've been learning their discipline since they were tiny, fidgety boys, their feet held up by their parents to encourage them to walk on their hands. A childhood of tumbling in cramped back yards and clambering on each other's shoulders followed, as did their instinct for imitation. Soon they were given seven-pound dumbbells to build their arm muscles and shown how to grip onto a bar. To learn balance and lengthen their spines they were encouraged to walk with objects placed on their heads - a wicker basket or a bundle of clothes. While their fellow apprentices endured the constant sight of a master's cane or the threat of being dropped on their heads their father instilled into them the acrobat's mantra of "practise, pluck and perseverance", teaching them the splits, handsprings, flip flaps and somersaults, throwing them around like shuttlecocks while still young enough to be fearless.

To learn the somersault the boys wore a thick belt with two rings attached above the hips with a cord threaded through each side. With the cords tied to the branch of a tree and their feet firmly on the ground the youngsters leapt forwards on their axis, supported by the cords. Eventually, after hours of constant, mind-numbing repetition, the cords were removed and they were encouraged to try the trick unsupported, leaping over obstacles onto a thick mattress, learning all the while that every small movement of the body has a value, that patience is a virtue and presence of mind is essential.

Now, after a lifetime of conditioning their muscles their bodies are lean and supple, their minds sharp and focussed. With their morning ring rehearsal finished the Lloyd brothers retire backstage to nibble on hard-boiled eggs and slices of cold ox tongue before continuing their exercises in the open air. In the corridor they are passed by Joe Ohmy's son Claude on his way into the ring, mounted on a fine-looking chestnut horse. At fifteen Claude is a chip off the old block, able to turn his hand to bare-back riding, globe walking, trapeze and – just like his daddy – the tightrope. Today his performance will include riding blindfolded over bridges and through flaming tunnels, providing some welcome momentum in between the much-anticipated acrobatic entrees.

The public's preference for acrobatics over equestrian acts is not the only change witnessed by Joe Ohmy since he first set foot on the Isle of Man. The visiting industry has wrought changes on the town of Douglas that have made it almost unrecognisable from the small smugglers' town of old. Last year the Packet boats ferried half a million people to the island to 'play' and it now seems that anyone with a spare room is prepared – for a tidy sum - to offer a bed to the 'cottonies' that flood here from all over the north.

And the fabric of the town itself is, of course, transformed. The Red Pier has been tarmacadamed, turning it into the 'Black Pier'; upper Douglas is lined with smart terraces and lodging houses, and the lower town is packed with hotels, shipping agents, refreshment houses and shops selling everything from bear furs to Italian cheeses. Pleasure oozes from every corner. Young men stroll the promenades in straw hats, blazers and white pants, arm-in-arm with young ladies carrying sun shades. They, in turn, are besieged by photographers, flower sellers, match girls, white-coated porters and shoeshines, all striving to part them from their hard-earned holiday club savings. During the day the roads bustle with cars and trams and in the evening a myriad of gas lamps illuminate the curved rim of the bay like a duchess's tiara.

Entertainment is as essential to this town's fortunes as its supply of fresh water. And to this end Mr Elphinstone's circus building has had a lucky reprieve. If the town planners had had their way the entire neighbourhood between the piers and the quay would have been cleared to make way for an extravagant tower – similar in ambition to the Eiffel tower – but the plans came to nothing and the circus has endured for another season. Though tired and unprepossessing from the outside it is still cheerful inside, decorated for the new season with colourful flags and banners and brilliantly lit.

With the changes in the town Joe Ohmy is aware that he too must change with the times. In the early days of his career audiences were ready to applaud any new trick the human body could command. Now, physical entrees are as familiar to the public as a loaf of bread - and just as commonplace, performed not only in circus but in every music hall and variety theatre up and down the land. It is increasingly difficult to develop acts that are fresh and new. Yet still the public - mostly men - come, drawn by the timeless appeal of jeopardy like moths to a flame. Under the lights, at the edge of human experience, immersed in the heady mix of smoke, sweat and flame, they can smell it, see it, feel it, the drama of life and death, the exhilaration that comes with challenging the human body to its furthest limits. Unlike the onlooker at a lecture, play or recital the circus spectator doesn't need to tax his brain but can simply enjoy the ride in all its electrifying glory. Which, fortunately for Joe Ohmy, is something he never tires of.

These days he also feels blessed to be joined in his enterprise by his whole family. Aside from his son Claude he is surrounded by women. His wife Diana, the company treasurer and wardrobe mistress, staunch in her affections and eminently practical; eighteen-year old Lizzie, a renowned horse trainer and elegant haute école rider; sixteen-year-old Ada, sweet Ada, who walks the rolling globe, and little Minnie, who, at eleven years old rides her trick pony with admirable confidence. Even baby Lillie, at just three years of age, is already imitating her siblings' balancing skills.

Following the afternoon performance the company disperse to their dressing rooms or the stables to briefly rest before warming up for the next show. They are hungry but eat frugally. Calisthenics and full stomachs do not make a happy marriage. By half past seven Ohmy's Circus is ready to mesmerise the public all over again and anticipating a good house. Six thousand people are rumoured to have disembarked onto Manx soil today and from the number of ships observed steaming up the Victoria Pier packed with smiling faces it seems highly likely.

The band is in fine, rumbustious form – some might say a little too rumbustious - as the audience shove their way into the auditorium and squeeze along the rows of plush self-righting chairs in the front stalls. Once they are seated 'King' Ohmy takes to the ring and quickly introduces the opening act, his son Claude, who proceeds to please them with his skilful riding. Next comes a troupe of amusing tumbling clowns, a young lady on a beautiful horse dancing a polka and Douglas favourite Toney Felix with his comical pony. Before long it is the novelty turn the audience have been waiting for, the acrobatic musical clowns The Heeno Brothers.

Behind the scenes James and Hugh Lloyd have been warming up in the green room for the past half hour, stretching and rubbing their limbs with horse liniment, doing push ups and pull ups and jumping on the spot. Their musical instruments are tuned and ready and their bodies are primed. They enter the ring and each immediately takes a seat on a wooden chair, adjusts his violin and launches into a familiar seaside tune which quickly has the audience clapping and singing along. After a few bars they rise to their feet and climb onto their chairs, balancing on one leg, guiding their bows under their knees and other comical gymnastic gyrations, playing all the while. They then jump to the ground and, without interrupting the music, perform the contorted manoeuvre practised earlier in the day in which their bodies become intertwined, gradually evolving into a position in which one violinist ends up sitting on his companion's back, the melodies flowing unabated.

To herald their finale one brother stands plum in the centre of the ring beneath the chandelier, the light glinting off his bow as his hands fly across the strings. He then lays down his instrument and takes up a small headpiece which he fixes in place with a band beneath his chin. His brother comes to stand before him and the audience falls quiet as they grip arms and with a small hop, and enormous mutual strength, his brother flips into a handstand above his head, legs stretched skyward, forming an exact mirror image. For a moment it's only the power in their arms that keeps them upright but then the topmost performer slowly lowers his head until it is placed firmly on his brother's. The strain on their bodies is such that it's impossible for them to keep still. Their limbs shake and their muscles bulge and ripple, shining with sweat under the lights. And then they let go of one another and, to improve his balance, the upper artiste parts his legs wide in an inverted version of the splits. The audience clap hesitantly but there's still more to come. A painted clown steps forward and passes the two artistes their violins which, to the crowd's astonishment, they resume playing as though they were standing on the stage of a music hall. To Joe Ohmy's delight the cacophony that follows is deafening.

During the interval the Lloyd brothers congregate backstage with a band of fellow acrobats who are due to perform in the second half. The Leglere troupe are a youthful ensemble of fine-looking young athletes led by

Leopold Leglere, a strapping male specimen, thirty-seven years old with powerful shoulders, slim hips and a rack of stomach muscles as solid as iron railings. Leglere is a colourful character. The son of an Austrian acrobat and an English mother, he was one of ten lively children raised to join 'the profession' and recalls a childhood practising his gymnastics in overcrowded, inner-city lodgings while his sisters sang and danced. Now his sisters are all burlesque dancers and Leopold leads his own troupe of acrobats, six in number, some of whom came to him at a young age from poor families who offered their children as apprentices.

For an hour prior to their performance the Leglere troupe prepare themselves mentally and physically. The boys are feeling the strain of months of arduous travelling on boats, trains and bumpy cars and it's a challenge to achieve the right mindset. Much of their routine involves supporting the weight of another person and their warm up is varied with stretches, tumbling, sit ups and lifting. It also involves a huge degree of trust and nerves of steel and Leglere insists on an atmosphere of quiet calm as they go about their work. Half a dozen youngsters are unlikely to succeed in building a human pyramid if there is any stress or antagonism between them. Although at times it's hard to concentrate. In the background they can hear the rise and fall of the crowd's reactions to other acts and it heightens the tension within the room. The Leglere troupe are following an ancient tradition that reveres acrobats as symbols of human perfection and in the hierarchy of modern-day acrobatics equilibrists such as themselves - who specialise in the art of balancing - are considered to be the true Olympians.

After a couple of minor entertainments in the second half it's announced, to a huge roar from the crowd, that one of the country's finest acrobatic troupes is to enter the ring.

Against a backdrop of dimmed lighting the young men move stealthily into the centre of the arena and climb onto a raised platform. As an expectant hush falls over the darkened space a bright light from above suddenly illuminates a breathtaking scene. Like a finely sculptured marble statue the acrobats strike a pose in which each performer is hand to hand, foot to foot, knee to knee. And then, to a backdrop of dramatic music, they begin to move, every tiny shift slow, deliberate, measured. Toes are pointed, limbs elongated, chalked feet and hands are placed with exacting care. In perfectly choreographed fluid movements they alter their positions to take one another's weight on their hands, feet, legs and shoulders, their taut muscles and tendons straining and quivering and glistening with sweat. The silence in the front row is as intense as the music, the spectators made increasingly conscious of their own physical shortcomings by the beautiful curved shapes created on the platform.

Under the limelight the young acrobats fix their eyes firmly on one another. Their strength is extraordinary but to balance on a partner's body with your bare hands also requires total concentration, tuned to the other person's breathing, their body and their timing. Just one moment of inattention and the artistic illusion will be shattered.

With the end of the music the tableau melts away, the acrobats slink off the platform and the audience break into loud applause. They're still clapping as a Greek god bounds into the ring. Leopold Leglere wears colourful leotards embellished with coloured braid, and wrist bands to absorb his sweat. There's not an ounce of superfluous flesh on him and his smile is wide and dazzling.

Behind him, with leaps and bounds, comes his loyal band of apprentices. Two perform the 'Arab somersault', taken from the side, spinning around the ring in opposite directions on alternate feet with no hands used. Others roll forward, head down and land, hands-free, on the nape of their necks while their team mates cartwheel or fly through the air in single somersaults. As they bounce onto their feet they wave to the crowd and are met with thunderous applause and whistling.

In the background two stage hands have dragged in a large metal frame fixed with a high wooden springboard which they set on one side of the ring. On the other side they arrange a ten-foot-square straw mattress, topped by a similar-sized feather mattress. Led by Leglere the boys line up behind the frame and, one by one, quickly mount up onto the platform from where they run down the springboard to gain momentum, hitting the end with both feet and launching themselves high into the air. The angle is precise and practised, to provide the perfect leverage. As they fly forward they use the weight of their heads to achieve two tight, forward revolutions, landing on their feet on the double mattress with bent knees before raising both arms in salute. A couple of the boys stumble but the ringmaster is on hand to right them and prevent them falling off the mattress. It's hard to believe the double somersault was virtually unheard of at the start of the century. Now, any acrobat worth his salt is required to master it.

The Leglere's complete their routine with a display of strength and balance that always has the crowd – especially the ladies – charged with that curious emotion that only acrobatics can inspire, a tense, sickening combination of trepidation and stimulation. Leopold Leglere takes to the centre of the ring and is joined either side by two of his younger companions. They link arms across their shoulders and brace their feet in the sawdust. The percussionists in the band launch into a drum roll and the musical director holds up his hands to quieten the other musicians. Two more acrobats leap across the ring and clamber nimbly up onto their team mates' shoulders where they quickly find their feet and also link arms. Finally, the youngest and smallest of the troupe, a slight, beautifully built boy, climbs onto the human framework and, grabbing an outstretched hand, springs up to join the second layer, then with great dexterity is helped up onto their shoulders to stand precariously alone at the top of the pyramid. For an anxious moment it seems the audience reaction could go either way. Although the act is skilled and daring it isn't exactly ground-breaking. But every crowd is different and Leopold Leglere is never short of admirers. When a clash of cymbals breaks the tension the spectators voice their approval and the performers wallow in the heady atmosphere, bolstered by the lights, noise and bright, animated faces.

For the next half hour the usual parade of jockey acts, lady riders, clumsy clowns and stilt walkers rolls on unabated and without incident. And then it is the much-anticipated turn of the famous Lloyd Brothers, masters of equipoise, engaged for "their first appearance in this country at an unheard of salary!"

As the gas lamps are turned up they illuminate two men in scarlet costumes and soft slippers, each lounging in the central 'v' of two slack ropes placed side by side. Their demeanour is so languid as to suggest they are settled on chaise longues in a comfortable parlour. Until, suddenly, one mimes checking his watch and leaps to his feet, jiggling on the swaying rope, urging his brother to follow suit. Balancing on one leg, they remonstrate in perfect harmony, the rope quivering beneath their agitated slippers, their 'spare' legs dangling loosely. Before long the Lloyd brothers have the audience eating out of their hands, not only by their ability to walk, sit and gyrate on the ropes but to flip their bodies in devastatingly accurate somersaults, exacting relieved gasps as their feet find purchase.

After a few minutes they are each passed a violin which they seamlessly tuck beneath their chins and proceed to play with gay abandon, still mounted on the swinging ropes. The whole act appears effortless but it is only a process of long, slow evolution and exhausting practise that has made it so. Now they are so in tune with one another, both literally and metaphorically, that they are oblivious to the boisterous crowd. Their performance is all consuming.

After the show, Joe Ohmy comes looking for them. He finds them in their dressing room sorting through the customary pile of love letters and scented notes that is the curse of the modern male acrobat – a curse, they concur, that they bear with fortitude! Joe announces that all artistes are invited to join the post-show supper and without hesitation the billet-doux are put to one side. Love can wait. Supper cannot. James and Hugh change out of their leotards and prepare to fill their hungry bellies.

Addendum

At the end of August Ohmy's staged a Benefit performance in aid of Noble's Hospital in Douglas. The house was packed.

On his own Benefit night at the end of the 1894 season Ohmy was presented with a diamond ring by local gentlemen as a token of their gratitude. To add to the sense of occasion it was advertised that the clown Toney Felix would walk from the Central Hotel to the circus on stilts, a hot-air balloon would be sent up from the circus and Claude Ohmy would give a trapeze performance on the roof of the building outside.

Ohmy continued to seek out unusual and sensational novelties. Within ten years he had even grasped the technological age, and began showing cinematographic views on a large screen in the circus. Scenes included hare coursing, hunting, motor car racing and local news events.

Toney Felix the clown went on to manage his own circus and a music hall in the north of England before retiring to Peel on the Isle of Man's west coast to run the Crown Inn (the early date of which is allegedly his own fabrication). He later moved back to England and died in 1911 at the age of sixty, prompting tributes that described him as one of the most famous clowns of his time. Felix, born Thomas Green, began his comic career at the age of ten, later becoming an accomplished high-flying gymnast, stilt walker and clown, appearing on both sides of the Atlantic with Hengler's, Ginnetts and the Barnum and Bailey circus. He once won a wager in the presence of over twenty thousand people by racing on stilts against a Birkenhead horsetram over a distance of one mile.

In February 1914 Leopold Leglere advertised for a smart, small boy of fourteen years or thereabouts to go on the stage and travel with him. The conditions offered included 'a good home with everything found'.

In 1914, at the outbreak of the First World War, Joe Ohmy was performing with a large circus in Spandau, Germany, with his son Claude and two of his daughters. All four Ohmys were initially held by the authorities and six of his horses were confiscated, although Joe later told the tale that Black Bess acted lame – as she had been trained to do – and was returned. He and his daughters managed to return to England but Claude, as a young man of military age, was interned at the Rhuleben Camp for the next four years. Ada never fully recovered from the ordeal and died a few years later.

When Joe Ohmy died in 1931 at the age of seventy-seven, circus celebrities past and present turned out for his funeral at Blackpool Cemetery. His obituary suggested there were few people better loved than Ohmy and described him as a warm-hearted, generous artist whose conversation sparkled with little gems of circus life. The reverend who took the service maintained that the God who made Ohmy, a man who provided pleasure for millions of people, was a God who had humour in his being.

Chapter Seventeen

THE WATER NOVELTY

1896 Thursday 10th September

The sound of the treadle machine rattles through the walls of the circus, as insistent as a steam train racing through the countryside. The short, squat figure hunched over the table barely pauses for breath, her small foot driving the treadle in a constant, steady rhythm, her pudgy fingers deftly feeding yards of plush, gilded fabric beneath the frantic needle. So much work done, yet still so much to do. Mr Hengler has offered many times to buy her one of the new electric sewing machines but her treadle has been her long-time companion and she has always politely refused. Rosina Short has never been afraid of hard work and her costumes will be finished on time, as they always are.

Rosina is a plump woman, tightly buttoned into a black dress with a large white lace collar fixed by a brooch at her throat. Her grey hair is braided and wound in a coil on the top of her head. Within the circus family she is fondly known as 'Aunt Vic' for her uncanny likeness to Her Majesty, but her cronies are largely unaware that in her slim, svelte youth she went by the more glamorous moniker of Madame Saroni, wife and assistant to William

Saroni, the great musical clown. As she works her way through the pile of bright costumes beside her she can't help but be reminded of her own younger self dressed in spangled finery, sparkling beneath the chandeliers, her hair glinting with bejewelled ribbons as Saroni induced the crowds to laughter.

Sadly, of course, with time, she outgrew the circus ring, and her costume - and her husband passed on, but for the last twenty-five years she's been happily occupied behind the scenes, as head wardrobe keeper and costumier to the Hengler family, firstly to Mr Charles and now to his son Mr Albert.

In the corner of her eye Rosina sees a tall lanky figure pass her door and pauses just long enough to greet Mr Albert as he passes by. The constant ra-ta-ta-tat of her machine drove him to the golf course early this morning and he's just returned to check on the cirque's water pumps before retiring to his hotel to change out of his plus-fours.

Albert is thirty-four, six feet one tall and lean like his father, with a thin, angular face, long forehead and full moustache. His boundless energy is legendary, as is his passion for sport but, unlike his father and older sister Jenny Louise, his horsemanship is confined to playing polo, being deemed too tall and awkward to be an equestrian performer. Fortunately, at an early age he found his calling as the circus secretary and cashier, and slipped seamlessly into backroom management. When his father died suddenly nearly ten years ago, the business was left in the hands of Albert and his brother

Fred. When Fred also died Albert was left to manage the whole enterprise on his own. After settling any debts he bought up all his father's establishments and circus buildings from the Hengler trustees and became the sole proprietor of the largest circus company in the kingdom.

And he has had a good run. In the past decade the name Hengler has become the by-word for circus entertainment par excellence and newspapers were quick to dub Albert the 'King of the Arena'.

But these are challenging times. The golden age of the circus is beginning to lose its lustre. The public are increasingly drawn to the new variety shows and music halls which are storming the country, and Henglers' pool of performers are also being lured away by these new avenues of employment. Albert's London circus has recently been forced to close, his two northern ventures are under threat and even the family's long association with Glasgow is no longer assured. Albert cannot afford to rest on his laurels.

In his father's day the ring was the domain of the horse, but it's been a quarter of a century since the name Hengler was emblazoned on a cirque frontage in Douglas and Albert has opted for something entirely different - water.

Of course, so much has changed since Charles Hengler built his cirque in upper Douglas. Then, the site – neatly sandwiched between two houses of God - was chosen for its proximity to the town's leading lodging houses and distance from the smoke and stink of local industry. Now, hundreds of new boarding houses and homes have sprung up along the elegant two-mile promenade that lines Douglas bay and Albert has been able to build his circus a stone's throw from the pier, sandwiched between the more lucrative, if less saintly, location of two prosperous hotels.

His decision to try the Isle of Man all came about thanks to the ill-fated 'Eiffel Tower', the proposed spire of iron and steel that was to have been built on Parade Street by a group of Manx visionaries. Unfortunately for the visionaries what they had in grand dreams they lacked in cold, hard cash. The project never made it beyond the foundations stage and the empty site was purchased by the Steam Packet shipping company. When the adjacent 'New Promenade Circus', leased by Elphinstone and Ohmy, was demolished earlier this year the way was literally cleared for a single replacement building of vast proportions to be constructed between Parade Street and Bath Place. In March Albert had the site surveyed, a month later the builders moved in and an area of more than two thousand square yards began to fill with an impressive edifice of iron and wood. Visitors swarming past on their way to the new harbour swing bridge would often cause a road block as they stopped to pontificate on the building and its progress.

By July the new cirque was ready to be unveiled to a curious public – and Albert Hengler looked forward to their reaction. Although approximately three storeys high the vast rectangular construction is of no great architectural merit, being outwardly plain and unimaginative, the only concession to aesthetics being small garden beds planted up around the 'grand' entrance facing the Peveril Hotel. It's inside that the magic begins.

Tastefully decorated in traditional blue, gold and cream, accented by gilt mirrors, swathes of luxurious material and gold tassels, the interior is literally breathtaking. In one sitting Albert can welcome more than three and a half thousand people to enjoy the delights of a Hengler show, with no balconies or any other structure to obstruct their line of vision. Wide staircases lead up to the galleries and a spacious promenade right around the interior allows the audience to move freely within the building. Twenty musicians can be accommodated in the large orchestra pit and behind the main auditorium are numerous dressing rooms, a wardrobe room, props store and stables for dozens of horses. Even in a town where ornate entertainment palaces are now commonplace Albert is confident the interior of his cirque can match any of them in opulence and comfort. Perhaps in these uncertain times such an ambitious building is a huge risk. But the Isle of Man is Britain's 'Holiday Island'. If he can't make it here he can't make it anywhere.

Having acknowledged Mrs Short at her sewing machine Albert Hengler proceeds straight to the pump room behind the auditorium. The water novelty that is the highlight of this season's programme is not only a challenging dramatic performance but a complex feat of engineering. His trusty mechanics are already hard at work, checking a large engine, boiler and pump and the water levels of two huge iron tanks stored beneath the tiered seating. Thousands of gallons of sea water have been pumped into the tanks from the nearby harbour and left to settle, then cleared of the seaweed, crabs and other flotsam and jetsam that sank to the bottom. Later tonight the water will be drawn up to the height of the gallery in wide steel pipes and used to create an effect that never fails to stun an unsuspecting audience.

One of the men working on the pump tips his cap to Albert before taking a spanner from the back pocket of his blue overalls to tighten a valve. Fred Cattle is a Hengler stalwart who has been with the circus for nearly twenty years. Aside from his role as Albert's chief mechanic he is also one of his best clowns, known in the ring as Comical Cattle, a born funny man with a talent for the grotesque. Tonight, his overblown antics will reduce the audience to tears of laughter but for now he has more practical matters on his mind – the pulsometer steam pump is a recent invention designed to run without attendance and if Fred is to be otherwise occupied in the ring it is vital that everything runs like clockwork.

Albert greets the other man with a warm handshake. Alfred Powell is his business manager, a solid, jovial fellow with a round, kindly face, black eyebrows and a thick head of greying curls. A relative of the Hengler family, Alfred has also been a loyal servant to both Albert and his father Charles before him, drawing on his own impressive circus pedigree and deep knowledge of every aspect of modern circus life. But it's his early career as a mechanical engineer that has enabled Albert to experiment with scenarios that would otherwise have been out of the question. And for that alone Albert will always be in Alfred's debt, for 'the water novelty' has proved to be his finest creation and his financial saviour. Admittedly water novelties, despite their name, are nothing new but Albert likes to think that his adaptation of the genre is uniquely his own. It all started with a dream, he likes to tell people, in which he envisaged the circus ring covered with a big mackintosh, filled by great columns of water rushing over the sides of the ring fence. Years of experimentation and fine-tuning followed, and now thousands of holiday makers in the Isle of Man are being treated to the culmination of his dream.

Having satisfied himself that the plant in the pump room is in good working order, Albert leaves his colleagues and heads for his hotel to change. His initiation into the mysteries of golf is just one of the many good things that have come out of his visits to the Isle of Man. That and the excellent trout fishing. And the cycling. And the cricket. If only he had more time. He pushes his way through the crowds on the street and hurries on.

The first patrons arrive for the evening performance with an hour to spare. They comprise a large group of young scholars and adult helpers finishing their annual School Day Out with a trip to the circus and by prior permission they have been able to enter the circus by an 'early door'. Although their day began gently in a leafy glen north of Douglas, it quickly gained momentum with a visit to a rocky seaside cove to watch performing sea lions. After tea at nearby refreshment rooms on the shore the whole party was bundled into conveyances and brought to the Parade where they were greeted by Mr Hengler himself, who teased them that they may leave the circus as wet as if they had been in the sea with the sea lions! Having been promised 'real water, real boats, real fun and fat policemen' the children are in a high state of excitement and not even the threat of a sharp ruler can quash their spirits.

The house fills up quickly. Special late trains have been laid on tonight to allow people from outlying towns to attend the circus and it doesn't take long for every seat in the pit, promenade and gallery to be taken. The boxes are last to fill, firstly with groups of smart new tourists from London and the southern counties and finally with local dignitaries. As the Mayor and Mayoress of Douglas are ushered into their box the youngsters are urged to be on their best behaviour.

The children are dazzled. The brilliance of the white light in the auditorium hurts their eyes, four giant gas chandeliers sparkling high in the ceiling and eight powerful arc lamps around the circle illuminating every small detail of their surroundings. The evening is still warm and their teachers are grateful for the ventilating contraption in the ceiling that circulates fresh air around the giant building. Over-excited students fainting from heat exhaustion is not something they wish to contend with.

The evening opens with the usual fanfare from Mr Clement's band, a blast of trumpet, bass drums and piano that instantly galvanises the audience into a heightened state of expectation. The children in the front row of the pit beat their small palms together and squeal involuntarily, their eyes shining. The teachers smile indulgently. They too are warming to the munificence of the circus atmosphere and are more than usually tolerant of such unrestrained behaviour.

The first half of the programme passes quickly in a whirlwind of activity, familiar faces and familiar routines interspersed with electrifying new turns. Young women in tall hats and plum-coloured velvet, majestic on glossy black horses that rear, fly and buck. Elfin girls that dangle from the back of their mounts to collect white handkerchiefs from the sawdust. Handy Andy the clown, pretending to do everything while doing nothing. Lumbering cart horses and small patchwork terriers that dance, fetch, carry and sing.

By the time the interval is announced the crowd is humming. They have a vague idea of what is to come but cannot imagine how it will evolve. As the ringmaster announces a pause in the proceedings the schoolchildren join a stream of bodies heading for the public lavatories, while the occupants of the stalls take up their privileged invitation to inspect the stables. Those who choose to remain in their seats try to catch the eye of the bon-bon sellers wending their way through the rows selling sweets and candied fruit from wooden trays.

As the cast gather behind the scenes waiting to return to the ring they are subjected to a final scrutiny by Mrs Short. All fifty members of the company will play a part in the 'water novelty' and she works with her usual zeal, kneeling on a rug in front of the performers, a thimble on her middle finger, her teeth clenched on a mouthful of pins as she administers last minute repairs to dropped hems and loose braid.

And then her time is up. The ring master is recalling the audience to the auditorium and everyone resumes their seats for the grand finale - the spectacle three thousand avid circus-goers have been waiting for.

The children settle back into their seats unsure of where to look first. During the interval the circus ring has been transformed into a scene that resembles the country glen they were playing in only this morning. In the centre, beneath a spreading chestnut tree stands a rough wooden building hung with cart wheels and iron gates. In front of the 'smithy' two burly men dressed in leather aprons stand either side of an anvil, striking steel tubes of various sizes with their hammers to produce a melody of extraordinary beauty. As the music reverberates around the cirque the artificial village green in front of the smithy fills with a large group of children, prettily dressed in white suits and dresses, who hop, skip and dance to the tubular music. Soon they are joined by a crowd of older revellers led by two actors dressed as a local squire and his lady, followed in turn by a young woman dressed in a bridal gown and a young soldier, her husband-to-be.

As it dawns on the audience that they are about to witness a village wedding, the mood softens and whispers of approval ripple through the crowd from the front row of the pit to the highest point of the gallery. But all is not entirely harmonious in this bucolic scene. For who is that following the crowd and looking decidedly shifty? Two tramps played by the circus clowns Fred Cattle and Funny Valdo, scruffily dressed in tatty suits, are shadowing the wedding party, their eyes darting all around them, their nimble fingers slipping unnoticed into unsuspecting bags and pockets. The children on the front row of the pit shout to the wedding party to alert them to the danger but the tramps give them warning looks, earning themselves a chorus of hissing and booing from the rest of the audience. With the happy party none the wiser they move on, drawn by the sound of bells ringing out from a realistic church façade placed alongside the smithy.

Once the bridal party have safely disappeared into the 'church' the tramps count their ill-gotten gains and stuff their faces with food laid out on a trestle table for the wedding breakfast. Fred Cattle can't resist playing the fool, and his antics with jelly and whipped cream cause the booing and hissing to mix with the first intimations of laughter. By the time the wedding party emerges from the church in a shower of rice the booing is replaced by enthusiastic applause. Dancing and merriment follow and the audience clap in time to the music. Order and decency, it seems, have been restored.

But it's not to last. The comic tramps have become too carried away with the festivities and as they tease the bridesmaids and continue with their carefree pillaging they're spotted by two passing policemen. The arrival of this mismatched pair - Constable McFat robustly played by Alfred Powell, adept it seems at both engineering and performing - and his skinny companion Constable McLean, the agile clown Alfred Chirgwin, brings gales of laughter from the audience. The thieves are searched, their bulging pockets emptied and to cheers from all around the cirque they're marched off to the lock-up.

The tramps' apprehension heralds a major shift within the ring. As the audience chat amongst themselves and their applause dies away the cast of characters slip from under the lights and out through the ring curtain, replaced by a team of fit young men who swiftly dismantle and remove the makeshift smithy and church and disassemble the chestnut tree. When everything solid is removed, ropes with heavy metal clips attached are lowered from the roof of the cirque and attached to the edges of the 'green', hoisting it up to create a false ceiling. As it rises into the air the young men drag a heavy lining over the tan-bark, smoothing it into place before another gang enters carrying a roll of thick India rubber sheeting which is laid out over the lining and pulled up over the walls of the ring fence.

As the audience stare in amazement at what now resembles a gigantic empty fish pond, a small 'island' is brought into the ring and placed in the centre, dovetailed on either side by rustic wooden bridges that connect with the ring fence. The young men leave the circle and a hush falls over the audience, who watch and wait, holding their breath for what is to come.

Suddenly a bright light illuminates a tall man standing at the side of the ring. It is Albert Hengler, the light catching arrestingly on a diamond breast pin fixed to his lapel. He raises his hand, pauses for a moment and looks dramatically skyward. The audience follow his gaze and as he drops his hand a giant waterfall explodes out of a pipe at the top of the gallery, the foaming cascade of water thundering down into the ring, illuminated as it falls by lime lights in a startling myriad of colours. Against the roar of the water the entire building erupts as one body in a storm of applause.

The children in the front row are caught in surprise. Some scream, twisting in their seats in an attempt to get away, clearly terrified at the prospect of drowning, while others sit mesmerised, their rosy faces fixed on the thousands of tiny droplets that create a magical rainbow above their heads.

The ring fills with frightening speed, white light from the chandeliers glinting like stars on the swirling whirlpool produced by twenty-three thousand gallons of rushing sea water. As it rises to just below the bridges Albert Hengler once again raises his hand and the waterfall stops as suddenly as it started. The whole process has taken just two minutes but where horses pounded just half an hour ago there's now a small lake.

The children who were keen to escape are now persuaded to remain by two men who approach the edge of the ring carrying live ducks which are released onto the water with much splashing and quacking. As the audience point and laugh at the birds the wedding party re-enters the auditorium and walk over the bridge to the island where they lay out a rug and set up a picnic. Frank Anderson, who normally plays the clown Handy Andy, has taken the role of the interfering mother-in-law and brings the house down with his wicked pantomime. Not that there's much time to dwell on his antics. From the sides of the ring a couple of small rowing boats are launched onto the lake and 'hired' by members of the wedding party then, to the astonishment of the audience, even a miniature replica of a Manx passenger steamer takes to the water and toots around the ring, the captain whistling for everyone to get out of the way. It's all very pleasant, highly enjoyable, innocent fun.

But a good circus spectacle is nothing without an edge of peril and uncertainty. Few people notice the fisherman who's entered the scene, until he flicks his rod once too often and too carelessly and appears to become entangled with some of the wedding party. A row breaks out, 'mother-in-law' protests loudly, and suddenly, with a loud splash 'she' is falling, arms flapping wildly, into the shallow water. The audience roar with laughter. As other members of the wedding party attempt to rescue the floundering actor they are inadvertently pulled in, dragging another poor soul in along with them. And then it's the turn of the two clumsy policemen to get involved. But Alfred "P.C McFat" Powell nurses a secret. As a teenager he lost his left hand in an accident and now wears a cork prosthetic. As one of the flailing party in the water reaches for his hand it comes away from his arm, leaving the already-soaked actor floundering and sending the audience into paroxysms of hysteria.

What follows is a chain reaction of pure pandemonium. When the bride enters the water, the groom follows, then the fisherman, the children and the squire. Within five minutes the entire wedding party is thrashing about in the shallow lake, hampered by quacking ducks and an erratic steamboat. Water sloshes in waves over the side of the ring fence, causing those unfortunates in the front row to shriek and holler as they attempt to pull their feet out of harm's way. To top it all off, while the audience still have laughter in their lungs, the two hapless constables join the watery melee, the smallest performing a terrific somersault, causing more waves and a new surge of hilarity.

Finally, when it seems the audience can laugh no more, the drenched, shivering company haul themselves up onto the bridges and line up to take their bow. Once, twice, three times they are recalled to take a well-deserved encore, smiling through chattering teeth. When the band eventually strikes up the opening bars of 'God save the Queen' the spectators wobble to their feet, drained and exhausted, their sides aching.

It's an outcome that Albert Hengler, warm and dry and enjoying a welcome bottle of bitter backstage, has witnessed a thousand times but it still brings him a profound sense of satisfaction. As does the diamond breast pin now sitting back in its box. The pin was a gift from the Queen after a command performance by his company at Windsor Castle ten years ago and is a constant reminder of just how far his hard work and imagination have brought him. Sadly, Her Majesty has never seen the water novelty, her bent being more towards horses, but he imagines she would probably find it clever if not amusing.

Albert carefully closes the velvet box and leans back in his chair, his long legs outstretched, and takes a slow, satisfied draught of beer.

On Parade Street, where dozens of cars are lined up to take circus patrons back to the railway station, the waiting horses are startled by a sudden hubbub. A crush of animated figures has burst out of the main cirque doors, their faces flushed, their hats askew and their clothing damp and dishevelled. They don't appear unhappy, though. Far from it. Parade Street will echo with their laughter long after the last car has disappeared onto the quay.

Within the walls of the circus every member of the company swiftly, and with practiced efficiency, swings into action to clear up the chaos that has brought such mirth. In the pump room the pulsometer pump is fired into life, quickly sucking the water out of the arena and returning it to the iron settling tanks. The props are then removed and the mackintosh sheeting is brushed clear of every last drop of water and rolled away. In the aftermath the auditorium steams slightly, a strong iodine-rich smell of the sea lingering in the air.

In the artists' dressing rooms the performers speedily divest themselves of their cold, wet costumes which are put through the mangle and draped on racks or carefully squeezed in towels and hung to dry in front of gas heaters. 'Aunt Vic', as always, is on hand to cast a critical eye over every garment and remove any that need mending before tomorrow's show. Her knees and swollen fingers ache but she's only happy once every last pair of trousers, blouses and jackets has been examined, every loose thread snipped and every button securely fastened.

Hengler's have only one more week of engagements on the Isle of Man before they close for the season and head to Glasgow. Many of the artists hope they will still be able to enjoy a Sunday ride-out with the circus cycling club before they leave, led by the indefatigable Mr Albert. But that's still another week away. Another week of equestrian magic and aquatic mayhem. Another week of daily dousings. Another week of full houses and happy, shrieking customers. Another week of laughter and exhaustion, escapism and sheer hard work. Another week of typically challenging circus life.

A week they wouldn't exchange for all the tea in China.

Addendum

Later in September the circus was attended by the Island's Lieutenant Governor Lord Henniker, the Honourable Miss Henniker and the Government House party.

The following year Albert Hengler replaced the wedding party scenes with something even more dramatic, an equestrian piece that told the story of Russian prisoners escaping the silver mines of Siberia and their pursuit through frozen rivers. The action featured prisoners, soldiers, horses and carriages plunging into water within the circus ring.

But Hengler could not sustain such extravagant productions. In 1902 his Douglas building was taken over by Messrs Powell and Connor and two years later, Albert Hengler was declared bankrupt, the cause of his difficulties ascribed to bad trade and heavy business expenses in proportion to takings. Within two decades Manx people remembered Hengler's Circus fondly as a form of entertainment that had completely passed away.

But his artistes carried on entertaining. Frank Anderson, the clown 'Handy Andy', toured America for four years with Ringling Brothers Circus before returning to the UK for a stint at Gilbert's Hippodrome in Great Yarmouth.

Fred Cattle endeavoured to make an indoor parachute descent with Hengler's Circus in Liverpool. The parachute was suspended from the ceiling and held open by cotton threads. On the first attempt he landed heavily on the ground and, complaining that there wasn't enough air in the building, had the windows opened. His next attempt ended with him landing heavily on seats vacated by the audience. For his third try the circus ring was thickly covered with straw mattresses but the wind caught the parachute and he missed them by a few inches. After that he gave up.

Alfred Chirgwin travelled widely for his clowning career and was in Germany when the Franco-Prussian War ended. He was remembered for his somersaults, his principal trick being thirty successive evolutions on a handkerchief.

Rosina Short died in Blackpool in 1922 at the age of ninety-one, having only retired earlier that year. She had been connected with circus life for over seventy years, firstly in the ring as Madame Saroni, and latterly as a wardrobe mistress.

In 1927 the Scottish Sunday Post published a series of articles on circus life written by Albert Hengler. He talked of the importance of family within the circus, especially in his father's time when families were so versatile they could carry whole programmes - mothers and daughters capable of riding, wire walking, trapeze and acrobatic work, and fathers and sons clowning, tumbling and juggling. Children, he said, were usually trained to the work from infancy, born into the same business as their parents, grandparents and even great-grandparents and it was common for them to also marry within the industry.

Albert also recalled a visit to Windsor Castle to give a command performance before Queen Victoria. To his astonishment he received a letter from the Queen's equerry beforehand, stating that Her Majesty only consented to the clowns appearing on condition that they didn't talk. Whimsical Walker was Hengler's leading clown at the time and Albert maintained it was the only performance in his long career in which he didn't crack a joke.

Albert Hengler died in Hove, Sussex, in 1927. Although in his lifetime he had brought pleasure to hundreds of thousands of people, he died in obscurity, without any fanfare or loquacious obituaries.

Thankfully, however, as with so many of his forgotten nineteenth century circus associates, his legacy of spectacular circus entertainment lives on.

Glossary

Glossary of nineteenth century circus words and expressions. For an extended version see www.sueking-writer.com

Note: The language of circus people, sometimes referred to as parlari, is not a written language, resulting in many variations of a single theme.

Antipodist – performer who juggles objects with his hands, feet and legs while lying on a bed or board

Approbation – enthusiastic applause

Balloon – a large hoop covered with tissue paper, held up for an equestrian to jump through

Bandwagon – the open-top wagon that carried the circus band in the parade

Banner – a long cloth held across the ring to be jumped over

Bare-backed – a horse equipped with a pad but no saddle or stirrups

Benefit – a performance at which a star performer is given some or all of the profits

Bill – a poster, usually pasted on a wall

Buffos – clowns

Canion – knee pieces joining the upper and lower part of the leg covering

Cavaletti ropes – ropes attached to a tight rope to give it extra stability

Circus – an ensemble of acrobats, clowns and equestrians performing within a circle

Cirque – the building or tent housing the circus

Corde Volante – French for 'flying rope', a slack rope fixed at a great height

Cracking a wheeze – a clown telling a joke

Denarlies or **dinali** or **denali** – money

Dona or **donah** – woman

Doing a mob – collecting money from onlookers into a hat

Doublet – a tight-fitting jacket

Duey – two pence

Entrée – an act

Equilibrist – a performer who balances on apparatus

Faked up or **fixed** or **fakement** – circus apparatus

Flip flap or **flick flack** – a backward handspring

Fleshings – flesh coloured tights

Gag – a clown's trick or physical joke

Gallery – traditional wooden seating in steps

Garters – narrow bands held across the ring in the same manner as banners

Goosed – when a performer is hissed by the audience

Handbill – a small poster, handed out as opposed to pasted

Harlequin – a masked clown dressed in a tight-fitting costume of diamond-shapes and spangles

Haute école – highly controlled horse manoeuvres, similar to modern dressage

Hippodrome – an arena for equestrian performance

Hup la, allez! – ready, go!

Icarian games – a performer lies on his back and juggles another performer on his feet. Known in America as the 'Risley Act'

Infant – a very young child performer

Jester – a clown who relies on clever use of words rather than physical activity

Joey – a white-faced clown

King Pole – the main support pole for the tent

Lacing – the system of eyelets and loops on the edge of a canvas top used to join canvas sections together

Leaping (performer) – an acrobat who jumps into the air with or without a springboard

Leaping (equestrian) – horse-jumping over fences and obstacles

Lofty tumbling – somersaults and springs

Mantle – a short cloak

Menagerie – a collection of wild animals, for display and performance

Motley – the colourful, eccentric costume of a clown

Omey or **omi** – a man

Pantomime – a circus 'play' depicting a scene or event, usually with a large cast and extravagant sets and props

Patter – words, often scripted, used by clowns

Pitch – the place chosen for a tent or performance

Polander – a performer who balances with a pole, stack of chairs, ladder etc

Professional or **pro** – a performer who makes a living from the circus

Queer the pitch – spoil it by interference or accident

Riggers – men employed to handle the ropes, canvas and mechanics of a circus

Ring fence – the wall surrounding the circus ring

Rope walking – performing on a slack rope or tight rope

Rosin – a type of resin, often used on stringed instruments

Rot – bad or contemptuous

Saulty – a penny

Slack rope – a low rope hung loosely to form a V

Slap stick – the 'magic' stick used by the harlequin

Spangles – tiny metal discs sewn onto a costume

Stand – the time that a show is at one location eg. a one-night stand

Still vaulting – mounting and dismounting a horse

Stock – the long scarf worn by an equestrienne

Style – to gesture to the crowd in acknowledgement of applause

Tanbark – light wood chippings on the floor of the ring

Tent men – workers employed to build up and take down a tenting circus

Tent master – the man in charge of erecting the tent

Toe rag – a bad person

Tourbillon – literally 'whirlwind' but used in circus as 'head over heels'

Tray saulty – threepence

Trunk hose – short bloomers allowing room for movement

Tumbling – acrobatics

Vaulting – mounting and dismounting a horse usually while it is in motion

Wheeze – a clown's joke

Author's note

My decision to illustrate the lives of real characters with a fictional narrative was not an easy one and one that may not sit well with historians. However, circus history is not a subject that lends itself easily to formal treatment. Quite frankly, it is a complex, tangled web that shifts on the wind. Nineteenth century circus folk were not always who they said they were. Names were frequently fabricated, changed, adapted or re-used. The number of Blondins, for example, is quite extraordinary. Dates, ages, times and places were 'tweaked' if it could make a better story for purposes of advertising. Claims were often grandiose, unsubstantiated and unquestioned. But at the heart of it all were real people - fascinating, hard-working, incredibly brave, entrepreneurial and dedicated people who pushed the boundaries to provide thrills and entertainment. Their stories deserve telling in a manner that befits their extraordinary lives and it is to their characters that I sincerely hope I have done justice.

(In attempting to bring these characters to life I am aware that I may have made some factual errors for which I take full responsibility, although I have referred to original source material wherever possible and made every effort to cross-reference my findings.)

Acknowledgments

Grateful thanks to Culture Vannin, to the knowledgeable staff at Manx National Heritage and iMuseum, the British Newspaper Archive, the Isle of Man Public Record Office, the Isle of Man Family History Society, the Isle of Man Victorian Society and all the many, many people who answered my obscure queries on everything from aerialist skin care to Victorian gas lighting.

Special thanks to my early manuscript readers for their tireless support, encouragement, suggestions and beady eyes; to Ruth, for her expertise and ability to translate my doodles into the striking cover that is everything I hoped for; to Words & Spaces for turning my words into a beautiful, printed book; to Suzanne for her generosity in allowing me to write while 'on the job'; to Deb for taking me to Circus Oz all those years ago; to David for the incredibly thoughtful 'boost'; to Gandey's Circus, keeping circus alive on the Isle of Man in the 21st century and blending the past with the present in the most thrilling way possible.

And the biggest thankyou of all to my wonderful family and friends for getting me to the finish line –

"hup-la, allez!"

Select Sources

These are just some of the most useful print and online sources I referred to while researching nineteenth century circus. A more comprehensive listing is available at www.sueking-writer.com

Digitised Newspaper archives

www.britishnewspaperarchive.co.uk

www.imuseum.im - (Manx National Heritage)

www.newspapers.com - (international newspapers incl. USA, Australia and New Zealand)

Records, Maps, Plans and Directories

Manx National Heritage

Isle of Man Public Record Office

Liverpool Library Central Record Office

Books

'Victorian Arena – The Performers. A Dictionary of British Circus Biography V.1' John Turner, Formby Lingdales Press 1995

'Circus Life' and Circus Celebrities' Thomas Frost, Chatto & Windus 1881

'The Tightrope Walker' Hermine Demoriane, Secker and Warburg, London 1989

'Belzoni - The Giant Archaeologists Love to Hate' by Ivor Noël Hume, University of Virginia Press 2011

'The Public Life of W.F.Wallett, The Queen's Jester' W.F.Wallett, ed. John Luntley, Bemrose & Sons, 1870

'A History of the Circus' George Speaight, The Tantivy Press 1980

'Olympians of the Sawdust Circle' William L. Slout, Circus Historical Society 2005

Isle of Man International Exhibition of Industry, Science and Art, Belle Vue, Douglas, 1892 Prospectus, Brown & Son, Douglas

Websites

www.sheffield.ac.uk - (National Fairground Archive, University of Sheffield)

www.vam.ac.uk - (Victoria & Albert Museum)

www.bl.uk - British Library collections

www.fairground-heritage.org.uk

www.circushistory.org - (U.S Circus Historical Society)

www.circopedia.org

www.circusfriends.co.uk

www.circusperformers.com

www.goodmagic.com - (circus language)

www.ancestry.com

www.blondinmemorialtrust.com - (tightrope walking)

www.labonche.net - (circus history)

www.archicirc.e-monsite.com - (circus architecture)

www.youtube.com - (video footage)

www.pbs.org - (video footage)

www.bbc.co.uk - (The Golden Age of Circus: Show of Shows BBC4)

Articles & Printed Ephemera

"A Lifetime Behind the Scenes" by Albert Hengler, series of articles published in the Scottish Sunday Post 1927

'The Clown's Story' originally printed by the Standard and reprinted in The Isle of Man Weekly Advertising Circular, June 13th 1871

'From Belle Vue Park to National Sports Centre 1889-2001' by John Wright 2003 (MNH)

'Old Douglas' the notes of John Frowde (MNH MD36)

'Training a Circus Rider – The Reminiscences of James Melville, Australian Bareback Rider' New York Times February 17th 1881

'A Holiday in Manxland' by John Foster Fraser (reprinted in Windsor magazine August 16th 1895)